Words for Wellbeing

Using creative writing to benefit health and wellbeing

edited by Carol Ross

foreword by Jim Eldridge

Contents

List of Illustrations   **Page**

A Cumbrian Guide to the Bliss of Solitude
by Pam Clatworthy

Close your eyes, and as the train
Pulls into Ravenglass
Steam-hissing to a halt,
Listen to the squabbling of dusty sparrows,
Warm wind wavelets caressing sand.
Breathe in the scent of roses
Enticing warm air.
Embrace the morning sunshine,
Taste on your tongue, the salt of life.

Close your eyes, and as you feel
The rough stone wall
Warm beneath bare knees
Listen to the bleating of fell sheep,
The curlew's haunting cry
As it skims the blue horizon's limit.
Breathe deep the velvet evening air
In the green fold of the dale.
Taste on your tongue, the salt of life.

Close your eyes, be still.
May peace absorb your solitude.
Let every pore of your being
Rejoice in the beauty of the land.
May you take your strength
Through ears and mouth and skin
And the heritage of a thousand years.
Taste on your tongue, the salt of life.

Foreword

Jim Eldridge

We have all personal experience of illness, physical or mental, either our own personal experiences, or those of family or close friends, and often the hardest thing can be the healing process that follows the illness. Whether it is recovering from physical illness, such as a broken limb, or a serious operation, or a draining illness, or emotional or mental trauma, in most cases it is the mind and the spirit that needs healing most. The clinicians call it PTSD, Post-Traumatic Stress Disorder, and it comes in various forms and degrees. Sometimes it can be so debilitating it seems impossible to continue living, sometimes it appears to recede into the background, only to surface when least expected.

Not so long ago, society was aware of the importance of convalescence: time spent letting the body heal, but most of all, letting the mind and spirit recover, however long it took. In those days Convalescent Homes could be found in most part of the UK. In recent times, as society's pace increases, and demands for *immediate* results are a constant, very little time is allowed for convalescence, for the body and mind to heal before someone is diagnosed as "well". Time, they say, is the greatest Healer. And that does not mean just time passing, time to become accustomed to grief, or to changed physical circumstances, but the time spent in the healing process. The time to get over the trauma, and then the time to adjust, to come to terms with whatever has happened. It is well-known that the healing process can be aided hugely if some of that time is spent *writing*, a catharsis to examine and hopefully help conquer the inner demons.

Carol Ross is one such believer in that process, and her work in bringing together the poems and prose in *Words for Wellbeing* is a much-needed and timely reminder in these frantic times that the healing process is not just physical; not just a case of mending a broken bone or treating a disease with the latest medication. The healing process should be holistic, and where complications –

often emotional – prevent that healing, then writing is a hugely powerful medical tool. Writing for Wellbeing is more than surface therapy; it is rebuilding the harm and the hurt, and helping Life to be grasped again.

Jim Eldridge is an award-winning writer. He has had over 250 TV scripts broadcast, both in the UK and internationally; and 250 BBC Radio 4 scripts broadcast. He has had 78 books published, mainly for children and teenagers, which have sold over 3 million copies. His television work includes *The Ghost Hunter*, *Julia Jekyll and Harriet Hyde*, and the sci-fi series *Powers* amongst many others. His radio work includes the long running BBC Radio 4 series *King Street Junior*, and the comedy classic *Parsley Sidings*.

His recent books include the *Disgusting Dave* series; the *Black Ops* series; *The Malichea Quest* series; the *My Story* series of historical fiction, and many more.

Jim was born in London in 1944. He and his wife live in Cumbria in England.

After leaving school at 16, Jim worked in a variety of jobs (stoker at a blast furnace, production line worker, clerk, transport manager; etc) before going to teacher training college. He taught in a variety of schools, primary and secondary, working particularly with children with reading difficulties. It is his despair at the rising rate of illiteracy (particularly amongst boys) and his passion for encouraging children to read that is behind much of his work as a writer for children and teenagers.

Full details about Jim's writing can be found at this link: www.jimeldridge.com.

Acknowledgements

I would like to thank the chapter authors for generously contributing their creative words, knowledge and personal experiences, and for being so encouraging, supportive and patient. I am also grateful to Sir Andrew Motion and Faber and Faber Ltd. for making it possible to include 'The Cinder Path' and to Penelope Shuttle and David Higham Associates for 'When Happiness Returns After a Long Absence' (see Chapter 4).

The book incorporates a wonderful anthology of over 50 poems and short prose pieces written by people from all over Cumbria. Far more submissions were received than could be included, and I would like to thank everyone who submitted creative work – not forgetting the artists who created the beautiful illustrations.

So many people have helped to bring this book to fruition that it would be impractical to mention everyone by name. I am grateful for the behind-the-scenes assistance of many, including: the panel members who had the difficult task of selecting the poetry and prose; colleagues, friends and family who helped with advice, ideas, and editing and proof reading; and county and school libraries, GP practices and colleagues who displayed leaflets asking for contributions to the book. I am also grateful for the support I received from Cumbria County Council and its recognition of the importance of writing and wellbeing.

I would like to thank the organisers of the Cumbria Partnership NHS Foundation Trust 'Dragons Den' and everyone who supported the Cumbria Partnership Year of Writing; because without the Year of Writing this book would not have happened.

And finally I dedicate this book, with love and thanks, to my family who have been wonderfully patient and supportive during the Year of Writing and Words for Wellbeing projects.

Carol Ross.

You Might Fly by Stephen Hanley

Everyone needs a moment
To reflect and re-focus
Know who we are, find yourself
What you could do with inner peace.

You know you've got what it takes
Try to make it through the haze
Just a chapter in a damaged book
Give it a try tonight, cos you might fly.

Think about the birds and blue skies
Take all the time, all the time you need
Cos I don't have to tell you time heals
Things just happen naturally.

Are you feeling a little better now?
Remember that it's all in the mind
You've won so many times before
So give it a try tonight cos you might fly.

You're not alone, you're not invisible
Don't be scared to speak the truth
Because its time they knew the real you
You don't have to hide anymore.

So give it a try tonight
Cos you might fly.

Making the Most of *Words for Wellbeing*
Marilyn Messenger

Wellbeing is at the centre of a balanced life. Taking care of our mental and physical wellbeing is essential. Our mental wellbeing in particular, and how we view ourselves, is fundamental because it has an effect on how we form relationships with other people and how we manage the inevitable ups and downs of our lives. Mental wellbeing, like physical wellbeing, involves maintaining reserves of energy and ability that help us to be resilient when life takes a challenging turn.

Creative activities have long been viewed as beneficial when we are worried or anxious, but writing has often been overlooked in this respect. Yet no one would argue with the idea that words are capable of creating something magical. Written or spoken, words can move us to tears with the beauty of their imagery or captured emotion and they can make us laugh out loud. Words often live within us, long after we have read or heard them, to kindle further thoughts or images. And all of this is created by human beings, fashioned from somewhere within us and often using the simplest of tools: a pen and a piece of paper.

Perhaps the very 'magic' of words is the reason why many people imagine that writing creatively is beyond their capabilities – they don't see themselves as wizards or sorcerers. *Words for Wellbeing* is a book which aims to show its readers that they can indeed write and, even better, that writing could help them towards an improved sense of wellbeing.

Words for Wellbeing has a varied selection of chapters, poems, images and prose pieces. There are accounts in the book written by people who have overcome major problems in their lives and who offer a moving insight into how this was achieved. Reliable, practical advice abounds and there are writing exercises to explore.

Some readers of this book may already enjoy writing and would like to help others to share the same rewards. There are chapters in

Words for Wellbeing which show how successful practitioners achieve this regularly.

Some chapters may awaken your interest straight away because they are particularly relevant to an existing need or situation in your life. Others that seem at first glance to be less relevant may turn out to be the most helpful.

You can read this diverse book from cover to cover, select initially from the contents listed, or simply dip into its pages for inspiration and encouragement. Above all, readers of *Words for Wellbeing* should quickly appreciate that they don't need 'special powers' to write, because they already have the ability to create with words. They simply need the encouragement that this book offers to get their words onto paper or to help others to do so.

Words for Wellbeing has been compiled to help people to discover and enjoy writing as a possible means of finding their way back to wellbeing. With chapters that inform and enlighten and creative writing to enjoy and inspire, this book shows that we all have the ability to write.

Finally, whilst not an exhaustive list, *Words for Wellbeing* is intended to be of help to the following groups of people:

- Those who would like to try writing both for pleasure, and as a means to help their wellbeing

- People who are unwell, recovering from a period of illness or experiencing stress

- Clinicians and therapists who want to explore the possibilities of writing therapy

- Educators, parents and young people.

Once encouraged to write, anyone can then discover that their writing has the power to amaze others, and frequently astonish themselves. How wonderful is that!

Brand New Start by Colin Bentham

What prey tell the morrow brings,
As I hear the flutter of tiny wings.
Birds that soar and fly so high,
And leave me here to wonder why.

Oh how I wish that I could fly,
And soar so highly in the sky.
And glide across the oceans blue,
Mountain ranges and deserts too.

Escape I must to live my life,
And leave behind this pain and strife.
But if the pain inside me dwells,
Shall I haunt these moors and fells.

Or shall the beach where ere I roam,
Forever be my lasting home.
Or shall the towns and cities be,
The final resting place for me.

But yet awhile I have to wait,
To reach my graduating date.
For then I will be born anew,
And all will see what ere I do.

For like a phoenix out of fire,
I'll finally soar and fly up higher.
My wings will spread so broad and wide,
All shall sense the coming tide.

For in my dreams I stand so tall.
And many people hear my call.
And all around the world will change,
But you'll find it not so strange.

For what I see will soon be here,
And all will know what I hold dear.
For what I have within my heart,
For us all a brand-new start.

Song from the Garden (After Blake)
by Elaine Trevitt

I waited for a bloom to spread
On a spent flower head
Mistaking it for a bud
When it was already dead

I cut off a tightly furled bud
Mistaking it for a spent flower
Failing to recognise the difference
My life in metaphor

Wellbeing Hobbies by Grace Deakin

One should always have a hobby
Don't sit around and stagnate
And if you still can get about
Gardening and walking are great

Take advantage of things you can do
If you can hold a pen, just write
Spelling and grammar don't matter
Poetry or prose is alright.

Writing is also a great help,
Particularly if chairbound,
Reading, another interest
Where satisfaction can be found.

So if your fingers still are good,
Arthritis not taken over
Embroidery is just perfect
I am sure you will discover.

And whenever you have a problem
There are so many aids to use
It may take a bit more effort
But just don't make it an excuse.

If the memory is good
One remembers all the past
The happy and the sad times
All the memories that last.

The ups and downs, the problems
Are everyday part of life
We wouldn't have the pleasures
Without a little strife.

Time by Debbie Mayes

In the space of a minute
one cat arrives, the other leaves.
They do not acknowledge each other
despite being from the same litter.
In the space of an hour
the sun moves down
behind the clouds that bring
shade to a brittle hot day.
In the space of a day
my mood changes from sad
to happy. The morning brings
the joy of anticipation.
In the space of a week
a butterfly has flown its last flight
and clematis buds have released
their large mauve petals.
In the space of a month
I have gone from well
to ill and back again.
Can animals be bipolar?
In the space of a year
my garden changes from snowdrops
to lilies and soft green leaves
to dry dark branches.
In the space of my lifetime
the oak will spread its girth
and allow its roots to run
along the ground like veins.

Chapter 1 – Word Power
Carol Ross

People write a lot – letters, diaries, poems, stories, 'to do' lists, shopping lists. And let's not forget electronic forms of writing – blogs, emails, Tweets, texts. There are so many ways to write creatively that lots of people do it all the time without even thinking that they're writing, and certainly without realising that it could be doing them good.

Writing is good for you! This book has come about because I passionately believe that and the aim of this chapter is to persuade you to start writing. Lots of people love writing and need no persuasion from me to do it. I want to persuade people who *don't* think of themselves as writers to give creative writing a try as a way of helping their health and wellbeing. It doesn't seem to matter what you write, it is the process of putting thoughts down in writing that does you good. It certainly doesn't matter how 'well' you feel you can write. When you write for your wellbeing you are writing just for *you* – so don't worry about spelling, punctuation, grammar and all that.

Although I do a lot of typing, I find that writing my thoughts down on paper has a calming effect on me over and above the effects of 'writing' on my computer. It may be that the rhythmic motion of my hand and the pen across the paper is soothing. But I also think that writing on paper allows thoughts to flow more freely. When I type I cannot resist going back to correct 'typos' which breaks the flow of my writing. If you do a lot of typing (or texting), I recommend that you try some freewriting (see later in this chapter) on paper every day for a few days and see how it makes you feel. Handwriting does seem to work differently to typing – but you should do what feels right for you.

Write what you feel you want – or need – to write, but try to write a little every day. The best way to encourage yourself to write is to practise. The more you write, the more you want to write. As a minimum, I would recommend you do 6 minutes of freewriting every day – perhaps in your diary/journal, or in a writer's notebook that you could carry around with you everywhere and use to note down any interesting things you see or hear that you might want to write about later. Freewriting is an enjoyable and powerful writing technique. It can provide inspiration for all kinds of more structured writing, such as: poetry, song lyrics, stories, essays, and writing about problems and worries.

Try to find a regular time to write – whatever time works best for you. Writing at the same time each day will encourage you to keep going. I find that writing at the end of the day can help clear my thoughts so I sleep better. Some people like to write first thing in the morning to find some calm to help them deal with the day ahead. Experiment with different times of day to find what works best for you and your life circumstances. But don't let yourself think you have no time to write – 6 minutes a day is not much time to find even in the busiest of days.

Experiment with different kinds of writing to find what you enjoy. Try something different. For example, if you like writing freestyle poetry, you could try writing a sonnet (Sweeney & Williams, 2003). If you like to sing, try writing song lyrics (Davis, 1988).

The biggest barrier to writing is finding the motivation to keep going. Setting aside a regular time to write will help with that, but you will also need to find some outside inspiration and support to keep going. You might think about doing a creative writing evening class or joining a writing group (face-to-face or online). Books, magazines and websites can give you inspiration to keep writing too (Capacchione, 1989; Morgenstern, 2005; Neubauer, 2006; Ross, 2012; Sweeney & Williams, 2003). Best of all might be to find someone else who wants to write so you can encourage each other. I have writing friends who live hundreds of miles away from me. We met on online writing courses and now we keep in touch and encourage each other by email.

This chapter is mainly about writing but reading books and listening to audiobooks can also help your wellbeing. I find that listening to an audiobook every night helps me get a restful sleep. Check out your local library: as well as having a large number of fiction and non-fiction books to borrow, it may have a range of audiobooks, and possibly some self-help books/audiobooks (Cumbria Libraries, 2012).

Freewriting

Freewriting means writing for a timed period without stopping to think, punctuate or correct your writing in any way. The idea is to just keep writing whatever comes into your head, without stopping. If you stop and don't know what to write next, just write: "I don't know what to write" a few times and more thoughts will come.

I mainly use two types of freewriting in my writing groups: (i) writing everything that comes into your mind for 6 minutes starting without any sort of stimulus (see Bolton, 2011, p. 33); and (ii) writing in response to stimulus words or phrases: 5 words, 2 minutes per word.

Try the following idea for freewriting. Look around you until something catches your eye – something that interests you. Look at whatever it is for a few seconds. Now, start to write whatever comes into your head and keep writing for 6 minutes. The idea is not necessarily to write about the thing you were looking at, but just to write down your thoughts. Remember: you are writing only for *you*, don't stop to think or correct anything, and spelling and punctuation don't matter. Don't worry if your thoughts come out jumbled and random. Just keep writing – you might be surprised by what comes out. Why not try freewriting every day?

Ideas for freewriting:

- Try freewriting in response to a random word or sentence you read in a book or newspaper.

- Freewrite in response to a painting or photograph.

- Or you could turn on the radio, and freewrite in response to the first story you hear. You might change the story a bit and write something different, or the radio story might remind you of a memory and you could write about that. See where your writing takes you.

- You might write a story, or a poem or something about your past or your future. Just write what you feel like writing, two lines or two pages – it's up to you.

- Choose a 'set' of words that go together and write for 2 minutes in response to each word (I find that 2 minutes is about 1" or 2.5 cm of hand writing on an A4 page). An example word set could be: wind, wave, sea, ship, shore. Freewriting from word sets can produce great inspiration for writing poems and song lyrics.

- Read a poem or listen to a song and then write in response to it.

Journals and diaries

If you only do one kind of writing for the benefit of your wellbeing, do this: write regularly in a journal or diary. A word of caution though: if you find that your thoughts at the moment are all negative, be careful what you write in your diary because you don't want to emphasise your negative thoughts. If you are thinking negatively try making it a rule to only write about positive things in your diary – even if the positive things seem quite mundane to you some days, like "I got out of bed today" or "I went to the shop to buy milk this morning". Celebrate the positives however small they may seem.

There are no rules for writing journals or diaries – just write what you want. The only rule you might want to set for yourself is to always date every entry. That way you can look back through your journal(s) and see how things have changed.

If you want to use a diary rather than a journal you need to choose one that will give you enough space to write what you want to write. Some diaries give you a whole page per day.

One disadvantage of a dated diary is that unless you write in your diary every day you will end up with blank pages. That's why I prefer to use a journal, which is just a diary with no printed dates – in other words a blank notebook in which you write your own dates. There are no wasted pages with a journal, and you can write as much or as little as you like each day with no restrictions on space. And there are no blank pages to make you feel guilty about not writing anything for a few days.

Journals come in all sorts of shapes and sizes. I like to use an A5 size spiral bound notebook with a pretty cover and plenty of pages. Some people like to use an A4 notebook, and some prefer a bound book because they seem more substantial. The choice really is endless.

If you decide to write in pen, rather than pencil, choose one with fast flowing ink because your thoughts always go faster than your pen! Writing in different colours can be fun – just choose the colour that suits how you feel that particular day. I have a pencil case full of pens and pencils so I always have lots of choice.

Journals don't have to just be about writing. Some people decorate the cover of their journal with drawings, ribbons, buttons, tickets, photographs, etc. I don't decorate the cover, but I stick souvenirs inside my journal – programmes, photographs, tickets, and so on. Sometimes I sketch something I've seen – my drawing skills aren't great, but my journal is just for me so it doesn't matter.

Ideas for what to write in your journal or diary:

- Write about what you did and where you went today. Add your thoughts and feelings, hopes and fears.

- Write down your dreams – this works best if done as soon as you wake up.

- On the hour, every hour, for one day write one word that sums up how you feel at that moment. Then towards the end of the day choose two or three of the words to write some more about (Morgenstern, 2005, p. 79, 11 March).

- Write about something that happened or a conversation. Next, imagine that you are the other person in the conversation, or perhaps an object that was there at the time – a coffee cup maybe. Now write about the event or conversation again from this new point of view (Bolton, 2010, p. 123).

- Write lists – your favourite films/books/people, your shopping list, things you want to do this year (Adams, 1990, p. 123; Bolton, 2011, p. 34).

- Write letters to your journal as if it was a best friend.

- Freewriting for a few minutes every day. Decide how long to write for and then just write whatever comes into your head.

- Make a list of all the important areas of your life, e.g., family, friends, singing, writing. Every day write about the next one on the list (see 'Topics du Jour' in Adams, 1990, p. 167).

- A potted history of you.

- A letter from (or to) yourself (as you are in the present) to (or from) yourself sometime in the past or future, e.g., a future when you are well and happy.

- The story of how you want your life to be in 5 years.

- The best or worst thing about the day in question.

- Include detail in your writing, e.g., what could you see, hear, feel, smell and taste at the time you are writing about? How were you feeling?

Writing groups

There are different kinds of writing group so if the first one you try is not for you don't be put off. Some writing groups *write* during their meetings, whereas other groups meet to *discuss* writing but don't write in the meetings. Some writing groups take their writing very seriously and their members might have had work published or be working towards publication. And some groups are more welcoming to beginners than others.

You could start a *Words for Wellbeing* (Ross, 2012) group yourself – it's much easier than you might expect. A writing group can just be a small number of like-minded people who get together to inspire each other to write. One person can take responsibility for bringing writing stimuli and writing exercises for the group to try, or the group members could take it in turns to provide writing inspiration.

The library could be a good place to help you find an existing group, or start your own group – they might be able to provide you with a room to meet, or display leaflets advertising your group. You might want to consider volunteering to lead a writing group where you work or study, or in your local hospital.

Comics

Making comics can be fun if you like drawing. Try this way of making a simple comic: fold a piece of A4 or A3 paper in half to make a 4-page booklet. With a fine black pen, draw a line horizontally across the middle of the front page. Next draw two more lines to divide the bottom half of the page into four equal rectangles or 'panels'. Now draw lines to make eight equal rectangular panels on each of the other three pages of the booklet. The big space at the top of the front page is for the title of the comic and the first panel of the story, which should set the scene for the whole story. Now continue the story through the booklet.

It's a good idea to plan your story first so you know what you are going to draw and write in each panel. Don't use too much text, mainly you will need speech bubbles, thought bubbles and some short pieces of descriptive or explanatory text where necessary, e.g., '...three days later...'

To make your comic more interesting and professional-looking, try drawing most of the small panels as individual rectangles separated by narrow strips of white space (rather than using intersecting lines to make the panels as described above), and leave the big panel on the front and two or three small panels on each page with no border.

If you find you enjoy making comics I recommend the book *Making Comics* by Scott McCloud (McCloud, 2006).

Blogs, social networking sites, etc.

People all over the world enjoy sharing their thoughts and experiences on the web. Many people find it helpful to share their problems on support websites and interactive blogs. They get support from the comments of others and find comfort from reading about people who have had similar experiences to their own. Sharing your thoughts online may not be for you. If you do post personal thoughts and feelings online, please take care what you reveal about yourself. On many websites it is possible to remain anonymous.

How can writing help your wellbeing?

We don't know exactly how writing benefits health and wellbeing, although many research studies have shown that it does. I believe that writing probably benefits different people in different ways, for example:

- Providing a 'flow experience' (see next section on research).

- Bringing enjoyment – sometimes during difficult times.

- Giving you something different to think about.

- Clarifying your thoughts and feelings.

- Helping you to learn 'Mindfulness' – "Mindful Writing works by writing down your thoughts and feelings as you experience them. This strengthens your sense of NOW. The more you can accept yourself as you are, the more you can change" (Beier & Birkenhead, 2012).

- Bringing a sense of calm and decreasing anxiety.

- Lifting your mood.

- Allowing you to discover or re-discover an interest – not just in writing but through the topics that come out in your writing.

- Bringing out topics that inspire meaningful and interesting conversations.

- Reminding you of happy times and positive memories.

- Giving you a chance to 'stretch' yourself.

- Letting you re-define yourself as a writer rather than as someone with this or that diagnosis.

- Giving you the opportunity to share thoughts with others (e.g., when you write in a group or share writing online).

- Encouraging catharsis, i.e., the purging of emotions or relieving of emotional tensions.

- Making it easier to 'open up' and talk to someone about your problems, e.g., therapist or counsellor (see next section on research).

Research

Research shows that writing can have positive effects on wellbeing (for some examples see: Lepore and Smyth, 2002; Harris, 2006; Lowe, 2004; Wright and Chung, 2001). No-one knows how writing works (King, 2002, p. 119), although there has been some interesting brain research done (Lieberman et al., 2007). However, what is known is that it is the *process* of writing that leads to wellbeing benefits, and not what is done with the writing afterwards.

Much of the research that has been done about the benefits of creative writing, has involved people being asked to write about negative events. But I agree with Laura King (2002, p. 131) who says that it's not necessary to write about negative emotions or traumatic events to gain benefit from writing. People also benefit from writing that inspires happiness or joy. I believe it's important to achieve a balance between writing that helps you deal with unhappy thoughts or problems, and more neutral or positive writing that creates a sense of calm or encourages positive thoughts.

Do you know the saying to be 'in the flow'? A flow activity is something that you do just for the sake of it, and which takes up your whole concentration. And 'flow activities' are good for you (Csikszentmihalyi, 2008). What activities do you do that give you that feeling of being in the flow? For many people, writing is a flow activity, and that could be partly how it helps wellbeing. But not everyone finds writing a flow experience. Find out what your flow experiences are – playing football, gardening, learning guitar – and spend more time doing them.

Encouraging people to write can help them clarify their thoughts and feelings and express them to someone else. A Danish psychiatrist called Peder Terpager Rasmussen, recognizing the usefulness of writing in helping clients to explore their personal experiences, developed a systematic approach to guided letter writing. Rasmussen explained that the writing "is only a pathway, a channel, or a means towards the therapeutic end of self discovery and self healing", and he introduced "the metaphor of using a train as a means to explore a country" (Rasmussen and Tomm, 1992. p.4). Writing could be the train you use to explore the country that is you.

Some research carried out with young people has shown that blogging can help aspects of wellbeing (Boniel-Nissim & Barak, 2011).

For an interesting discussion on a theoretical model to explain how mindfulness can lead to positive change see "Mechanisms of mindfulness" by Shapiro, Carson, Astin and Freedman (2006).

So far, most of the research on therapeutic writing has been carried out in the USA and I feel that therapeutic creative writing is less advanced in the UK than in the USA. However, I find it encouraging that the National Institute for Health Research (NIHR, 2011) has commissioned an evidence synthesis or systematic review of research on the use of therapeutic writing in long-term conditions.

Conclusion

There's no doubt in my mind that writing is good for you. I hope I may have convinced you of the therapeutic benefits of writing. Go on – give it a try!

References

Adams, K. (1990). *Journal to the self: Twenty-two paths to personal growth*. New York: Grand Central Publishing.

Beier, A.; Birkenhead, E. (2012). *Mindful writing*. Retrieved 4 February 2012 from http://www.wordkit.co.uk/our-services/mindful-writing/

Bolton, G. (2010). *Reflective practice: Writing and professional development* (3rd ed.). London: Jessica Kingsley.

Bolton, G. (2011). *Write yourself. Creative writing and personal development*. London: Jessica Kingsley.

Boniel-Nissim, M.; Barak, A. (2011). The therapeutic value of adolescents' blogging about social–emotional difficulties. *Psychological Services*, 1541-1559. Advance online publication. doi: 10.1037/a0026664. Retrieved 26 February 2012 from http://www.apa.org/pubs/journals/releases/ser-ofp-boniel-nissim.pdf

Capacchione, L. (1989) *The creative journal: The art of finding yourself*. Van Nuys, CA: Newcastle Publishing.

Csikszentmihalyi, M. (2008). *Flow: The psychology of optimal experience*. London: Harper Perennial.

Cumbria Libraries. (2012). *Cumbria Libraries Well Read books on prescription*. Retrieved 4 February 2012 from http://www.cumbria.gov.uk/libraries/wellread/well_read.asp.

Davis, S. (1988). *Successful lyric writing. A step-by-step course and workbook*. Cincinatti, OH: Writer's Digest Books.

Harris, A. (2006). Does expressive writing reduce health care utilization? A meta-analysis of randomized trials. *Journal of Consulting and Clinical Psychology, 72*, 243-252.

King, L. (2002). Gain without pain? Expressive writing and self-regulation. In S. J. Lepore & J. M. Smyth (Eds.), *The writing cure: How expressive writing promotes health and well-being* (pp. 119–134). Washington DC: American Psychological Association.

Lepore, S. J.; Smyth, J. M. (eds.) (2002) *The writing cure: How expressive writing promotes health and well-being*. Washington DC: American Psychological Association.

Lieberman, M. D.; Eisengerger, N. I.; Crockett, M. J.; Tom, S. M., Pfeifer, J. H.; Way, B. M. (2007). Putting feelings into words: Affect labeling disrupts amygdala activity in response to affective stimuli. *Psychological Science, 18*, 421-428.

Lowe, G. (2004). Health-related effects of creative and expressive writing. *Health Education, 106*, 60-70.

McCloud, S. (2006). *Making comics*. New York: HarperCollins.

Morgenstern, S. (2005). *The aspiring author's journal* (translated by G. Rosner). New York: Harry N. Abrams.

Neubauer, B. (2006). *The write-brain workbook. 366 exercises to liberate your writing*. Cincinnati, OH: Writer's Digest Books.

NIHR (2011). *Therapeutic writing for people with long-term conditions*. (call for proposals, HTA No. 11/70). Retrieved 28 January 2012 from http://www.hta.ac.uk/funding/standard calls/11_70cb.pdf

Rasmussen, P. T.; Tomm, K. (1992). Guided letter writing: A long brief therapy method whereby clients carry out their own treatment. *Journal of Strategic and Systemic Therapies, 11*, 1–18.

Ross, C. A. (2012). *Words for Wellbeing*. Retrieved 22 January 2012 from http://www.cumbriapartnership .nhs.uk/words-for-wellbeing.htm.

Shapiro, S. L.; Carson, L. E.; Astin, J. A.; Freedman, B. (2006). Mechanisms of mindfulness. *Journal of Clinical Psychology, 62*, 373–386 .

Sweeney, M.; Williams, J. H. (2003). *Writing poetry*. London: Teach Yourself.

Wright, J.; Chung, M. C. (2001). Mastery or mystery? Therapeutic writing: a review of the literature. *British Journal of Guidance and Counselling, 29*, 277-291.

Half a Pair by Adam

Problems come and problems go
As life proceeds, we want to know.
Why after studies by great brains,
One simple question still remains.
One teaser they cannot unlock;
The mystery of the absent sock.
For every man who has a pair
Has known the day
When one's not there.

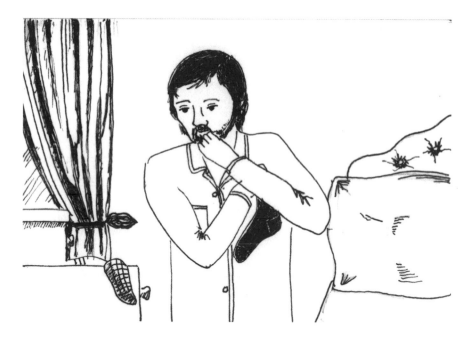

A Very Special Day by Hazel C. Perry

Warm. Soft. Safe. A shuffling movement at my side. My eyelids creak open; Susan is climbing up onto my chest, grinning down at me with her five little white teeth in her pudgy face. I look into her beautiful blue eyes, one with a little smudge of brown like a painter's palette, and I'm relieved to find that again I can greet her with the same joy and delight which radiate from every fibre of her little being. She'll be a year old next month. As she settles at my breast for her morning feed, I lay my head back onto my pillow and doze. I give myself permission to rest, to drift in the dim morning light as I nourish the baby at my side.

A soft thud from the next room. I hear footfalls padding across the carpet towards the door. Susan pops off my breast and throws her soft body across my chest, quivering with excitement as our bedroom door slowly opens. "Who's coming to see us?" I call in a singsong voice. Susan shrieks as her sister's head pops round the door, and Rose is scarcely less thrilled to see her. "I woke up and Dada was gone," she informs me as she snuggles into my bed. "Yes my love," I wrap my arms around her and bury my nose in her strawberry-blonde hair, "He got up early and went to work."

The girls are sleep-refreshed and lively; Rose, who will be three in a couple of months, is running round and round our mattress, steadying herself on the wall as she stomps over my head, and stumbling over my legs with her long, slender legs, while Susan, comparatively a little chubby ball, tumbles around amongst the bedclothes. Rosie yells, "I'm bouncing like Tigger!" and lands, with a chuckle, on her bottom. Susie cackles at her sister's antics and reaches out to try and pull her hair. Each morning they play the same game, and each morning it's as fresh and joyful as when they first discovered it. Susie becomes quiet, pensive, and grunts a few times. That's my cue to get up and fetch the clean nappies!

Changed, dressed and delightfully breakfasted on soya yoghurt and organic bananas from the vegebox, we convene in the living room. For many months now, this was my most difficult time. How would I pass the day? There were so many chores to do. I felt lost and listless, alone and afraid. I felt I had nothing to offer my two beautiful children. I felt so worthless, pointless, forlorn. Exhausted, I lay on the floor and wept, staring glassy-eyed at the television, which gave me but little comfort, and waited for my husband to come home. I changed nappies and fed my girls, and somehow completed the seemingly insurmountable tasks of sorting the washing and the household, stressed and frustrated, irritable and sad. I cannot put into words the pain I felt at finding myself unable to enjoy my little ones. How it hurt me to watch them play and smile, laugh and sing to each other.

But not today! I pack a few nappies and wipes, a picnic and some water, pop fleeces on the girls and strap Susan into the baby carrier on my back. Rose's sweet face lights up as I sit her on the stoop to put on her pink sparkly wellies. "Are we going in the garden?" she asks. "We're going to the park", I reply with satisfaction. Not long ago, I was simply too afraid to go outside. House locked up, Rosie's tiny warm hand in mine, we set off down the road. Like a lioness, I instinctively look around for dangers from which I must protect my offspring. My mind wants to show me pictures of the horrors that might unfold . . . a car out of control crashes onto the pavement; an angry dog comes growling up behind us.

Through my counselling with Sue, I have learned I can take charge of these fears. It's okay, I say quietly to myself. I take a deep, calming breath. Everything will be okay. Soothed, I carefully cross the busy road with my two precious charges, and watch Rose skipping away into the distance in the safety of the park. She looks so tiny out here in the big, wide world. She is fascinated by every detail of her surroundings, and I am warmed by her curiosity and enthusiasm. Having observed the swans and the ducklings, we reach the playground. The air is fresh from the previous night's rain, and I rub down the apparatus with a towel I have in my bag. I place Susie into a swing as big sis scampers off to slide down each of the three slides in turn. A delighted shout of "and a little bit more!" drifts across to us as Susie carefully grasps the metal chains. She smiles and giggles as I push her higher and higher. Her laughter gives her the hiccups.

Eventually my children tire of their play, and we head home. There's just time for a quick nappy change before Dada arrives home, and an exhausted Rosie tells him all about her adventures while I prepare the evening meal. Susie had a nap in the carrier after our picnic, so she potters about happily, pulling at her father's beard and chewing on her toys. I feel alive as the onions and garlic sizzle in the bottom of my pan, and savour the satisfaction of chopping fresh vegetables for my curry. Everyone is pleasantly full as Martyn takes a very sleepy Rosie up to bed and reads to her, and I eagerly anticipate our evening together as Susie drops off in my lap. I feel contented as I look back on my day with my beautiful children, and I am so very grateful that I can look forward to another one just like it tomorrow.

The Moment by Robert Armitage

All existence exists in the moment.
The last one's extinct in the past.
The next one, to come, has never begun.
The moment, forever, will last.

Memories are there in the moment.
Anticipations and predictions are too.
In the presence, of now, are the questions of how
things happened and what will come new.

Eternity's born in the moment,
conceived in a timeless embrace.
Beauty is truth in the moment:
Love, the wine of its grace.

So let's make a toast to the moment,
a presentation, to the present, with cheer.
It'll never be past, it always will last:
The moment is evermore here.

Chapter 2 – Write to Learn! Not Learn to Write!
Gillie Bolton

Once upon a time a weary traveller came upon a lovely peaceful village just as her thoughts began to turn to supper. A villager was standing at his garden gate enjoying the last of the evening sun. Our traveller stopped to enjoy the profusion of vegetables, herbs and fragrant flowers in the garden.

"You're a good gardener!" she volunteered.
There was no answer.
"You must have some lovely suppers from all these wonderful vegetables!"
Again no answer.
"I know how to make soup from a stone."
Aha, she'd hit upon a magic formula to create a response, in the form of a hard stare and a grunt.
"Well, you need a lovely smooth stone and to wash it well first."
This time the stare was accompanied by a glance at the garden and a questioning frown.
"Would you like me to show you?"
The gate was grudgingly opened just enough to let her through, and a stone searched for, washed and placed, upon instruction, just covered with water in a large pan.
"Um, well now we could do with flavouring this water; I saw a huge patch of herbs over there, and a small carrot and the sort of tiny onion you'd normally throw away."
You know the rest of the story. Little by little the wily traveller encouraged the gardener to fill the pot from the garden, and even to add some home dried beans and cured ham. They sat down later to a magnificent feast, chattering away to each other, and both very pleased with themselves: the silent gardener having found his words.

Creative healing writing is just like the fable "*Soup from a stone*". All it uses is our ordinary everyday words. Yet the action of writing, in the sort of way described below, can charge those humdrum words with magic. Just words on a page, put together with love and trust and care, can help us learn things about our lives, memories, thoughts, feelings and fears we didn't know before, or that we sort of knew and had forgotten, or that we knew only too well and never wanted to think about. Putting them on paper is a beginning of sharing, and can make such things easier to share with other people; and a burden shared is not only a burden halved, but it brings companionship as our two characters above discovered.

Why write? What to write? How to begin writing

Creative writing for personal and professional development – therapeutic and reflective – uses the tremendous power of creativity to help us to understand ourselves better – our thoughts, feelings, memories, ideas, inspirations, bodies, spirituality, relationships with others and our society. Making things creatively not only makes us feel good, but also gives insight and inspiration which ordinary everyday thinking and talking cannot.

Writing can help us pay proper attention to our own selves – privately. Humans are fabulously complex beings: we know, remember, feel far more than we realize. Yet much of this is stored inaccessibly, especially at times of stress or, most particularly, trauma. Writing can encourage our closed internal doors to slip ajar, or even open.

Our minds are rather like Covent Garden Royal Opera House, London. Most of the time we live and work in the auditorium – that lovely crimson and gold space – unaware that behind the stage curtain there are vast spaces (two and a half acres!) unknown to us, where all the workings of the Opera House go on: three massive stages, umpteen rehearsal spaces, practice rooms, offices, canteens, costume, scenery stores, and so on. It takes specialist enquiry to gain admittance to the essential areas beyond the wings of the stage.

Writing helps open the curtain to our mind's vital and huge backstage areas because issues seemingly impossible to share with another person can be first be aired relatively fearlessly with a piece of paper which never gets bored, angry, distressed or shocked, and its potential impeccable memory is impersonal. I say 'potential' as writing can be ripped up, burned, or flushed away: just creating it without rereading helps. Writing can be read and reflected upon, perhaps developed, redrafted, perhaps later shared with trusted confidential other, or group. Writing's privacy makes it qualitatively different from conversation, which will be remembered idiosyncratically; and we cannot be asked to forget what we have heard.

Thinking is also private, but it's hard to focus, and even harder to remember reliably.

Allowing words to fall onto the page and then seeing what's there can feel like playing around, like dancing, singing, or playing an instrument. If musicians play, why can't writers?

Stress or anxiety can make it hard to voice problems and fears, so they stay damagingly locked inside. Sometimes, on the other hand, we need to express ups and downs far more than others have time or patience to listen to. Paper and pen are endlessly patient, present, and never judge.

Expressive and explorative writing helps gain permission beyond the stage curtain also because it comes more directly from the body, via the hand. Our mouths are also part of our bodies, but talking is more likely to be censored by the controlling forces in the mind. The late poet laureate Ted Hughes said "The progress of any writer is marked by those moments when he manages to outwit his own inner police system" (Hughes, 1982). That police force (or Opera House usher) will be on duty far more with speech than with writing. He/she is much less on the lookout for the written word.

> "One of the first things Gillie said which really resonated with me was that 'people will always write what they need to write'. I guess she meant that the activity of writing has so much therapeutic potential anyway that just putting pen to paper with the right intentions can be useful and cathartic. She encouraged us to just write, to disregard the 'inner critic' and let things flow without necessarily knowing where it

would take us. She also stressed that we must chose our audience carefully both in terms of the level of understanding that we pitch the writing at (writing for a teenager would be very different from writing for other healthcare professionals for example) and the disclosure that may be involved in inviting a third party to read it."   I.S.

How to start

Six minutes free writing

This is a good way to begin every single time you write. It's how poets and novelists write, it's how many academics and professionals write reports. It gets the pen or pencil moving over that space that is daunting to every writer: a blank page. It can note and temporarily store safely some of the muddle of thoughts which can otherwise dominate. It can capture insights or inspirations which seem to spring from nowhere; these can then be developed in later writing. Many have called it the *splurge method*.

Put the pen on the page and write with no forethought, planning, and certainly no awareness of grammar or form. A list might come out, or seemingly jumbled odds and ends; our minds often jump about before we find a path through. Whatever it is, it will be right; this writing is about your own experience, memories, feelings, thoughts, ideas, fears, hopes; and you are the world authority on them. It need never be shared if you don't wish, and need never be reread: it's completely private.

"We then did a 6 minute writing exercise. I honestly can't remember the brief but as someone who is approaching a big birthday I have started to wonder where my life is going and ponder some of the choices made and lessons learned. I wrote some thoughts about these which were too personal to share (and we didn't have to share which was good) but were certainly helpful to me. I think there is something about seeing life choices and dilemmas written down which condenses them into universal themes, e.g., passion versus stability or the drive to inclusion versus the urge to stand alone. Having done this and summarised some fairly deep

36

existential issues in 6 minutes flat I felt strangely free as if by naming them I had divested them of some of their power." I.S.

- Take the pen and beautiful notebook or file paper, or whatever materials you feel like today: experiment with what works best for you.

- Choose where to sit: under a tree, at the kitchen table, somewhere miles from home or office. Listen to what you feel like doing.

- Choose a peaceful time when you KNOW you will have at least 20 minutes, UNINTERRUPTED, and ALONE.

- Make yourself comfortable in whatever way is right for you.

- WRITE whatever comes into your head for six minutes WITHOUT STOPPING, without rereading, as far as possible without thinking about it. Don't sit and think AT ALL before you start: put the pen or pencil on the paper and start writing, in mid-sentence if necessary. ALLOW YOUR WRITING HAND TO DO THE THINKING FOR YOU.

- Your mind hops around, so well might this writing. Write WHATEVER is in your head: descriptions; shopping lists, moans about traffic, weather, children, colleagues; an account of something that happened to you; last night's dream; work or dinner plans: it doesn't matter what it is. Don't stop to question anything: write without thinking.

- Since you don't think in sentences or logical sequences, neither might this writing. Only include punctuation, correct grammar and spelling which occurs naturally. FOLLOW the FLOW for six minutes.

- If you get stuck rewrite your last sentence, or look up and describe the first thing you see.

- You will never write a wrong thing. You are the authority of what is in your head, no-one else: you can't get it wrong. And no-one else is going to read it anyway, unless you expressly decide otherwise later.

And now... three exercises

Here are the exercises we did at the Writing in Healthcare Conference (Penrith, Cumbria, March 2011), and some wonderful examples of writing from generous people who typed them up and sent them to me. The exercises were chosen to be appropriate for both individual people and professionals wanting to reflect upon their practice. So – please try them all.

1. What weather are you now?

If at this moment you are not a person but a weather or season – what would you be? Perhaps a vibrantly growing spring morning? Perhaps a cyclone? Put your pencil on the page and write whatever comes – in note form perhaps, or as a list.

> "I am a very very still perfect summer day with a very slight suggestion of possible thunder ahead, calm and clear. I am a long day in the holidays.
>
> Most people would love to be that sort of day. But, I feel bored. I am too long and too perfect. And I want something elemental to happen, a new breeze to refresh the air, a wonderful cloud to pass by, a tree to move, or wave.
>
> Why won't the trees wave to me?
>
> Notes: I spent some time reflecting back on this about two days after the session....
>
> Writing this piece helped me to understand some of the deeper feelings that are brewing inside me. Reflecting and relating this to childhood, helps me integrate what I'm feeling, rather than being disturbed by emotions. Also it was a reminder to me that Life is powerful and it is time to wake up from the Dream!" Lisa Rossetti

> "Gillie asked us to write a sentence about what weather conditions we could best be described as. This simple task proved unexpectedly meaningful in that most people chose

mixed or transient states such as my own description of 'misty with some sun behind, waiting to come out'. I guess this was a useful way of getting us to think about how we were feeling and how to tune into the intrinsic creative potential within us all (as perhaps alluded to by the sun waiting to come out in mine and other people's examples)."
I.S.

2. Describe an occasion in your life

Think of an occasion in your work or in your life, interesting and fairly characteristic of your life or work. If it's your work – really the kind of event which is the reason you do your job and gain satisfaction from it. For me, I might choose an occasion like the March 2011 Penrith Conference. As with the *six minute writing*, allow your hand to decide what you want to focus upon, rather than sitting and thinking what to write about, let your hand scribble – telling you what you think.

Now – write it as if your reader were either a child who has asked you about your job or an aspect of your life, or a young school age person considering entering your profession, or doing what you do best (preparing a bed for onions for example). Tell the story of the event as fully as you can: put in any details you recall, and remember you have five senses – so sounds, colour, smells, tastes, texture might be important.

Really try to imagine you are writing for that child or young person – with appropriate language and simple story form.

Now read all your writing to yourself, including the six minutes. Alter or add to it if you like, always being positive about it, never negatively critical.

Then share it with someone else you can trust, if that seems appropriate. And write something else!

3. Talk to your 'Wise Internal Helper'

One part of your two and half acres of backstage (or backmind) wisdom is the garden of your 'Wise Internal Mentor' or 'Helper'.

We all have one; too few of us really make contact with this wise part of ourselves.

Write a brief letter to your Wise Internal Mentor, telling about a time when you were really puzzled, or even in confusion, undecided, anxious, unsure of yourself, feeling others did not understand you perhaps, or feeling alone.

Now write a letter to yourself from your Wise aspect. Try to allow your hand to write what needs to be written. Just let it flow, remembering no-one else need ever read this, and if they do, only after you've carefully read it to yourself thoroughly.

Read all your writing to yourself, including the six minutes. Alter or add to it if you like, always being positive about it, never negatively critical.

Share it with someone else if that seems appropriate. And NOW write something else!

> "Dear x,
>
> If you were best able to help me you could explain why my parents set me up to fail in life, didn't want the best for me and are still threatened by any sign of my success. You could explain this in a way that allowed me to still love them. You would help them to talk to me (really talk) and facilitate an open dialogue of the kind we are never likely to have... . What part of me was in those unhelpful interactions too? I need to know that in order to truly learn from it. After this you'd hug me and hold me and we'd go for walks seeing the woods and the flowers and the streams... . After all this I'd know that you had always been there for me and would always be there for me. I'd know not to grieve that which felt curtailed (relationships, career goals, choices not taken) because I am now in a better place and the very best is yet to come." I. S.
>
> Reply from x: "Firstly let me say how pleased I am that you are thinking these things and locating these difficulties where they belong – outside of yourself. I have always

thought of you as a shining star full of promise and potential. Don't let others zap it! We don't choose our family and in some ways you got a poor deal but it's made you who you are. They didn't act any better because they couldn't be any better. They were young, feckless, dogmatic and damaged. They look back on some of it with something akin to regret, but admitting that is a different thing. Pride is important to them and prevents the apology you often feel you need... . There are a variety of ways to be sorry just as there are a variety of ways to be strong, but then you already know about that."

"Having written these I felt like a load had been lifted from my mind."   I. S.

And, here is a reply from V—'s Internal Helper:

"Dear V—

I can read between the lines your sadness and some embarrassment that you still revisit your happy memories. My hope for you is that your give yourself a break from the criticisms that only you make.

If I were with you now, I would take you in my arms, old friend, and let my shoulder become damp with your tears. I would run you a bath. I would make you a lasagne. When you emerge all pink and child-like, I would offer you wine and sit with you and hear your stories. And it wouldn't matter how many times or how many ways you dissected the rise and plummet of your Grand Love.

I would buy you Tulips and take you shopping. I would buy you a book and write words in it that would comfort and warm you when you felt cold.

I would be your Mother (a good one) and your sister (a good one). I would be your daughter – your imagined one – and I would sit with you by the fire, sit with you in your silence and sleep with you till your tears run out.

I won't leave you V— till you realise that your forays to the past only succeed in you ignoring your future. And that's ok. There is time enough.

Time to be shiny and brightly polished again." V—

Find your own smooth garden word-stones, write them with care and loving lack of worry about grammar or similar. They will help you become "shiny and brightly polished again," and perhaps even "take a load from your mind." They will help you find what you didn't lose, and to discover a self you'd forgotten you knew.

References

Hughes, T. (1982) Foreword. In S. Brownjohn, *What rhymes with secret*? London: Hodder & Stoughton.

Tendril of Hope by Penelope Elias

No gardener I
However much I try
But I did once espy
A Wandering Jew in bloom,
Creeping up my garden wall.

Tiny blue flowers in profusion
'Midst bright green leaves trailing in confusion
Dispelling my gloom
Whilst my fears began to pall.

This unexpected sight suggested things just might
Turn out all right
And that there could be room
For hope to blossom after all.

Dear Tummy by Laura Jobson

Dear Tummy,

People are starting to stare now. You're not just big, you're gargantuan. You move and shift of your own accord, you cause all sorts of bother, and on more than one occasion you have wiped out an entire shelf of wooden toys and gifts.

The lovely, cute and button-like cargo you're carrying surely can't warrant a bump of such gigantic proportions? Can it?

I have done my best to distract myself form your burgeoning size. I have decorated the nursery, I have framed scan photographs and I have embarrassedly flapped my arms about in a swimming pool full of other rounded women. Some of their tummies were smaller than you. One might even call them petite. One woman had the gall, (or I suppose some might call it 'self-confidence') to wear a bikini in there! I don't know how she dared.

I think it's only right that we come to an agreement: you shrink as soon as possible. I think the magazines call it 'snapping back' to a size eight. If Uma, Myleen and Angelina's tummies can 'snap', I don't see any reason why you can't. And don't try cowering behind the argument that you weren't a size eight to begin with. That just won't fly.

And one more thing. I don't recall asking for stretch marks. I hope you're pleased with yourself, Tummy, when I have to spend a good ten minutes of every day smothering you in sticky substances. What with pelvic floor exercises and heartburn, I think I've got just about enough to deal with, don't you?

Thanking you in advance of your cooperation,

Laura.

Our Life Together by Dave Miller

Every day we sit and stare
Me over here you over there
My sitting up
You laying down
Me with a smile
You with a frown
You there waiting for tea
Getting it ready all down to me
But we seem happy and carefree
You still laying there waiting for tea
Every day we sit and stare
Me over here you over there

Laying there day and night
Wearing glasses such poor sight
Hearing is also getting bad
A world of your own, how sad
You watch the telly in your own way
Who, what, what did they say?
Story telling getting bold
4 o'clock getting cold
Put the heating up
Tea please i need to sup
Every day we sit and stare
Me over here
You over there.

You with your lies and stories you tell
On your couch not feeling well
Friends call for coffee and to chat
Sitting all still in their clothes and a hat
Meal in the oven ready to eat
You with a corn hurting your feet

Every day we sit and stare
Me over here you over there
Phone ringing who can it be?

Flashing lights you can't see
Answer the phone it's on your chair
Just remembered, must wash your hair
Pills to put up, you need a hand
You think you were picking up sand
The usual thing, pill on the floor
Your friends again knocking at door
Must ring the doctors you have a sore head
But not bad enough to put you to bed
Scalp all red needing an itch
Dont like running might get a stitch
Never mind, we still look and stare
Me over here and you over there

Pen to Paper by Dave Miller

Dark thoughts in a dark place
Wonder if it shows on my face
Cloud descends over my head
These thoughts I must shed
Pen to paper a way out
Writing non stop a gagged shout

Thoughts on paper writing fast
A reason for my unlucky past
Writing them down helps the pain
Helps to lift darkness to smile again
Meeting people of a like mind
Everyone happy and oh so kind

This writing has helped me well
All my family they can tell
A time for me to feel at ease
If only for me to please
When times are dimming, cloud descends
Pen to paper reminds me of friends

46

Coming Home from Hospital by Pam Clatworthy

A poet believes that when we are away from home our
surroundings miss us as much as we miss them.

The house was glad to see me back.
Warm carpet stroked my feet
massaged my soles,
Refreshed my soul.
"Welcome home," it whispered
"you will remove my dust
and I'll be yours again."
The turquoise curtain brushed my cheek
"Life hasn't been the same without you,
I've been quite blue,
I've missed your loving hands
That draw me close to you."
Even the bath taps gurgled with delight
At my return and welcomed me.

The garden was a different matter.
I felt hostility in the border.
An air of quiet vexation from the pink carnation,
"Red sedum has invaded my space,
Dig it out now, it clashes."
The clematis whipped my head
"Where were you when I needed your support?
I went all floppy
While you were away."
Nettles stung my ankles
In the long wet grass. Cruel brambles
Carved red zips in tender flesh.
I wept but then a robin came
And sang at my return and welcomed me.

Writing it Down Helps! (Eileen Norman)

When my 20-year old son first went into psychiatric hospital it was a very stressful time for me as well as for him. It was hard to think straight but I knew I had to because he couldn't. It seemed important to understand what was going on and to be able to act and speak on his behalf. I found it helpful to keep a notebook with me so that I could write notes about what was happening whenever I went to the hospital and met a doctor, nurse or social worker. It was all so new to me, I had no idea of what to do and I think the notes not only helped me to hang on to some sort of reality but also to remember things that I was being told – information about illness, medication, people's names, things I wanted to look up on the internet when I got home. Also, right from the beginning people asked me lots of questions. Everything from what his birth was like to what he was doing last week. So I wrote other things down in my notebook: lists of any illnesses and traumas he might have suffered, dates of stressful events and so on.

After a while, when it became obvious that this wasn't going to be a short term situation, I decided to put all my notes onto my computer so that I could refer back to them more easily. At this stage I also started to write a bit about how I was feeling. Sitting at the computer gave me some quiet, reflective time on my own and sometimes it seemed easier to try and sort out my feelings and share them with the computer than with other people. It wasn't that people weren't caring. My husband, other family members and friends were fantastic – very sympathetic and ready to let me talk – and I needed that a lot. But I felt I couldn't ask them to keep on doing it all the time. They had their own lives to get on with. Also, they had their own feelings about the situation, so inevitably they brought their own emotions into conversations with me, which sometimes complicated things. In spite of lots of support from friends, family and professionals over the years I couldn't help feeling "no-one really understands." Actually, I don't think anyone does unless they have a loved one who is in a similar situation. So, the computer journal became a useful outlet for me.

I have now kept this journal for 10 years. There are huge gaps in it, for weeks, months and even years. This is because I mostly wrote in it when things were pretty difficult and didn't need to do it so much when we were all jogging along more smoothly. As time went on I realised there was another value to keeping an account. When I looked back it helped me to understand patterns of behaviour and illness – my son's and my own.

About three years ago, when my son became established on a medication that suited him, our whole family's quality of life slowly improved – with a few dips along the way of course. I then found the journal useful as a way of recording my hopes and fears for the future and as a reflection on what we've all been through. A few months ago I sat down and read through the whole thing for the first time ever and shed quite a few tears. It taught me a couple of lessons, though: that things can and do get better; and that writing it down helps!

A Teardrop by Alison Gawne

A teardrop rolls graciously and slowly down the side of my nose. I sniff, another one follows. That teardrop is despair, fear, loneliness. Pain, pain, pain, anger. What am I angry at? This prison, this establishment I want away. I want the teardrop to fall graciously and slowly onto the floor. As it dries up, so goes my hurt, as the teardrop shrinks and melts away, so will the fear, the pain, the loneliness, the wanting to be a baby wrapped safely in the arms of her mum. I want safety. I want love. I want security. I want to watch that one tiny teardrop disappear, and as it melts into nothingness, then I know I can feel at ease, as one, as me, Alison. I am proud of that teardrop, even though I know there are rivers more to come. I know that one teardrop went on such a special journey. Do you know why I know that? I know that because that teardrop was part of my own journey. I cherish it, and own it.

A Letter to Manic Depression by Katie Metcalfe

Dear Manic Depression,

This shouldn't come as a surprise. You knew it would happen eventually, me writing about us. From the looks of things, we're in it for the long haul. You stepped in at the same time as when anorexia started to hump my leg, whine at me and beg for a place on the bed. You are like someone exotic that you meet on holiday, with cut glass features and the gorgeous but deadly voice of a demon. We've had quite a few years together, and you didn't take kindly to the medication at first, spitting out the yellow and white, pin prick sized pills. But now, you both get along like a house on fire, making me sick and the whole world woozy when I forget about the both of you meeting up. Even if I forget for just a day, you make me regret it with all of my being. Sometimes, you need so much attention; I am disabled from doing anything else with my 24 hours. When we have our tiffs, I walk and count the reasons why I love life, and living becomes much more intense and wonderful. I smell, taste, hear, touch and see things I missed before. I laugh more, and make the most out of everything, good and bad. When you want attention, you never need to ask me. You just get it. My world has to stop to accommodate the darkness and silence you insist on. But how can I hate you when I understand myself, life and other people so much better? Now that I have seen the world without sun and felt my mind stall when lacking inspiration. I can appreciate what others take for granted: a quiet mind, shopping for a lemon squeezer and talking through bad moods. I know the times will pass when all the birds are brown, when emailing people is better than seeing them in person and getting out of bed to do anything is torture of the highest degree. You have worked my body to get over you, like a relationship you thought would last forever or a broken ankle you thought would never heal or a treasured book pulled apart from the spine. You are often like an ill child or kitten that has lost its mother. I don't get annoyed when people say they are feeling a tad depressed, because I know they're not really depressed, and I'm happy for them, that you and they haven't properly met. I know not talking about you is stupid. It would be like not wanting to walk again after splintering your spine. Or not wanting to see Picasso in his work space, or not wanting a Thermos of tea on the top of a cold, blustery mountain. I talk about you because I want evidence of you, everywhere, so people can get to know you and understand you and not be afraid of you. Sometimes, I wonder why you picked me, but finding the answer to that is as difficult as eating a frozen bar of chocolate with a fork, so I won't bother wondering anymore, while I am still smitten with life.

Katie

Sleep Now by John Masson

Sleep now
Be Still
Let rest repair pain's corrosion

Take time
To heal
The wounds of last night's skirmish

The battle is not yet over
And in its ending lies another hurt
To win is to lose

So sleep now
Be still
Regain your strength

But when you wake
Know
You do not fight alone

Chapter 4: Slip Free of That Lamb's Clothing, For Truly You Are a Lark

An Account of Poetry Therapy in Practice

Victoria Field

The title of this chapter is taken from a poem written in less than ten minutes by Mel J. in a workshop on poetry therapy. Part of the alchemy of writing is that that combination of words and ideas didn't exist before the workshop and yet now they are in print. You, the reader, may find them intriguing, puzzling, magical, strange or uplifting. They may even prompt you to write something in response.

Poetry therapy is a technique that works with the human impulse to seek solace in poems, stories and songs. Many of us have a favourite poem stuck on the fridge, folded in a handbag or pocket or know some lines and phrases by heart. Poetry therapy involves reading or listening to the work of other people and also draws on our instinct to write ourselves in response to intense emotion. Remember the outpouring of poems after the death of Princess Diana, or the diary-keeping of teenagers.

Reading and writing together can open an imaginative space where healing can take place, especially when working in a supportive group setting, with sensitive guidance. People are often astonished at how quickly poems, whether read or written, can yield insights into the concerns and dilemmas of our human condition. Sharing these with others is immensely affirming. A poem by someone else shows us we are not alone and conversely, our own writing reminds us that we have individual and unique experiences and our own voice in which to express them.

The techniques of poetry therapy can be adapted for many kinds of groups or individuals. I have worked on a stroke unit, with people with diagnoses of dementia, in care homes and with adults with learning disabilities, where I 'scribed' poems or worked entirely orally. For the purposes of this chapter though, I'm going to discuss how a particular group (of writers and therapists) responded to two specific poems. These were presented as part of a one-day workshop that was run in Truro, Cornwall in June 2011 by myself and my friend and poetry therapy mentor, Geri Chavis.

I'd like you to join us on our journey through these two poems so that you can feel, as well as read about, the way in which poetry therapy can work.

 The first poem is by Andrew Motion. I invite you to read the poem slowly and, if possible, aloud to feel the words in your mouth and get a sense of its rhythms and cadences. Pay attention to any emotions or memories it stirs in you. Imagine telling someone else about how you react to the poem. What would you say?

Passing On

By noon your breathing had changed from normal
to shallow and panicky. That's when the nurse said
Nearly there now, in the gentle voice of a parent
comforting a child used to failure, slipping her arms
beneath your shoulders to hoist you up the pillows,
then pressing a startling gauze pad under your jaw.

Nearly there now. The whole world seemed to agree –
as the late April sky deepened through the afternoon
into high August blue, the vapour trails of two planes
converged to sketch a cross on the brow of heaven.
My brother Kit and I kept our backs turned to that
except now and again. It was the room I wanted to see,

because it contained your last example of everything:
the broken metal window-catch that meant no fresh air;
your toothbrush standing to attention in its plastic mug;
the neutral pink walls flushed into definite pale red
by sunlight rejoicing in the flowering cherry outside;
your dressing gown like a stranger within the wardrobe

eavesdropping. That should have been a sign to warn us,
but unhappiness made us brave, or do I mean cowardly,
and Kit and I talked as if we were already quite certain

you could no longer hear us, saying how easy you were
to love, but how difficult always to satisfy and relax –
how impossible to talk to, in fact, how expert with silence.

You breathed more easily by the time we were done,
although the thought you might have heard us after all,
and our words be settling into your soft brain like stones
into the bed of a stream – that made our own breathing
tighter. Then the nurse looked in: Nothing will change
here for a while boys, and we ducked out like criminals.

I was ordering two large gins in the pub half a mile off
when my mobile rang. It was the hospital. You had died.
I put my drink down, then thought again and finished it.
Five minutes later we were back at the door of your room
wondering whether to knock. Would everything we said
be written on your face, like the white cross on the heavens?

Of course not. It was written in us, where no one could find it
except ourselves. Your own face was wiped entirely clean –
and so, with your particular worries solved, and your sadness,
I could see more clearly than ever how like mine it was,
and therefore how my head will eventually look on the pillow
when the wall opens behind me and I depart with my failings.

Andrew Motion

'Passing On' taken from *The Cinder Path* ©Andrew Motion and
reprinted by permission of Faber and Faber Ltd.

Here are some comments from the Truro group (sent by email
after the workshop):

"This poem really spoke to me. Its raw and vivid description
and images - the beautiful flowering cherry contrasted with a
dressing gown hanging like a stranger in the wardrobe –
summoned emotions and memories associated with deaths I
have known. The stranger in the wardrobe line in particular
transported me into a memory I have – associated with losing
someone close to me, a dear friend – and looking in her
wardrobe after she had died..." Anne Taylor

"I felt I was holding my breath during it, but one thing I could not ignore was my powerful reaction to it. Anger. I have tried to work out what that was about, but it seemed mainly a reaction to what I felt was the insensitivity of the nurse. I was a nurse about 20 odd years ago and I left mainly because I felt pressured into being part of a conveyor belt type, dehumanising system..." Mel G.

"'Passing on' was a wonderfully honest and clear-eyed account of what it's like to be around a parent who's dying – the strange mixture of heightened emotion and humdrum everyday reality. It brought back very vivid memories of being in that situation myself..." Tom Scott

The participants were encouraged to stay with their own personal responses rather than any intellectual assessment of the poem. When discussing a poem, there is no 'right answer'. Pieces are chosen to be immediately accessible to the reader and also to have some ambiguity. Things get interesting when one person says "oh, that's a sad ending" and someone else says "no, it's hopeful!"

One of the characteristics of a 'good' poem for therapeutic purposes, is that it generates more ideas on each re-reading. Andrew Motion's poem is especially rich in this respect.

"Today, visiting the poem for the third time and preparing these notes to send I'm struck by the title 'Passing on' and I think, other than the obvious reference to the popular term for dying, what is passed on? Who passes on? Can we choose not to 'pass on'? (seemingly not!) What are the implications of this inevitable 'passing on'? ..." Liz Burns

Obviously, a poem like this can stir painful emotions but, paradoxically, it can feel safe because we are reading someone else's words.

"It gives a name to our feelings and experience and connects us not only to the poet but to the group who are also responding to the poem. It can allow us to make sense of something that hadn't formerly been put into words. When the poem is there, in the room, it offers a certain distance between the words and the emotion or experience. In that distance something happens; we re-process it in some way that is always ultimately beneficial..." Hilary Farmer

Now I invite you to read the poem again and pick out any lines or phrases that 'speak' to you, for whatever reason. Make a note of these – or if this is your book, underline them.

This suggestion brings into play unconscious processes and concerns. The lines chosen might only have a tangential relationship to the theme of the poem but relate powerfully to the concerns of the reader.

"...'the vapour trails of two planes / converged to sketch a cross on the brow of heaven.' These words entailed a story about myself, quite early in my career, at a big teaching event and how what was being demonstrated ... intersected with my own personal, and heavily embodied, experience..." Liz Burns

"...'a child used to failure' ... we discussed how often the word failure was used and how it permeated the poem. I didn't feel like tackling the actual subject of the poem directly. I did respond to a kind of subtext of disappointment and failure in the poem ..." Angela Stoner

Next, I invite you to choose one of the lines or images and use that to make your own poem. In poetry therapy the emphasis is on spontaneity, seeing where your writing takes you – there are no rules. The only constraint is the limited period of time for writing. In the group, we took 10 minutes.

The choice of line is entirely up to the participant. We are therefore in control of what material we choose to write about. This can work in a subtle way. If there is material or subject matter we are wary of, although deep down we do want to explore it, we can approach it obliquely. In the Truro group, many people wrote about loss of a loved one but, indirectly, thinking about the cherry tree, the gin and tonic and awkwardness of speech, all suggested by Andrew Motion's poem.

"I identified eight phrases which I could have used as starting points for my own work ... Interestingly, the two phrases I was most moved by ('your last example of everything' and 'I depart with my failings') were the two which for reasons of self-care and appropriateness of getting too involved within the workshop context I left aside ... I chose 'Your own face was wiped entirely clean' to use as a springboard. This still related to my husband's health, and touches on similar fears, but seemed an easier option..." Ruth Hausmann

The next stage of the process is to share what's been written. Again, we can choose whether to read out, talk about the process or remain silent. This part of the session can be very releasing as often we are able to write what we can't easily say. The 10-minute time limit helps to put a boundary around complex and difficult emotions.

Many people in the Truro group wrote movingly about personal losses.

"This poem ... prompted me to write about the death of my friend – a woman I had known for 30 years – at the age of 45. I wrote about visiting her mother and family after her death and about looking in her wardrobe. The finality of death, the shock of it is never easy to accommodate. Writing has helped me to get my head around it, not just the grief, the missing, but the mind-blowing concept that death is. Sometimes no matter how many times a difficult experience is revisited in your head it is not resolved – writing somehow salves the pain; there is something about the creative act of writing, the recording of a special memory or profound moment on the page that feels helpful." Anne Taylor

Reading personal material aloud to a group is both immediate and ephemeral and can be cathartic, and often that's enough, the poem has done its job. At other times, the resulting writing might be edited or shared elsewhere.

"I wrote (this is intended to be read very slowly but I don't know how to suggest that):

Sleeping, morphine-drunk, your face etched blank,
I exhale, empty.
I yearn to be snowbound."

Ruth Hausmann

"Failure

A child used to failure,
finding life a little bit more complicated
than it needs to be –
the child whose egg wobbles on the spoon, dropping
it almost before the starter's gun.
The child whose shoelaces unlace themselves –
who cannot start a fire or tie a knot –
who has a talent for forgetting things –
for losing them.
To keep engaging with the daily muddles,
the detritus left in failure's wake
takes courage. Almost superhuman courage.
Such courage you could say
that such a child needs no
En- couragement."

Angela Stoner

Here is the second poem I presented to the group at the end of a long day of reading, writing and discussion. I'd like you to read it, again aloud if possible, perhaps more than once, and pay attention to the emotions it arouses and again imagine what you would say to someone else about the poem.

When Happiness Returns After a Long Absence

When Happiness returns, after a long absence,
she's a very small creature indeed,
an orderly marching ant,
scurrying beetle, or web-spinner –

Let her be a spider,
learning to spin her web again,

lodging modestly behind the washer-dryer
in the back-kitchen,
earning her keep by waste-disposal of flies

Let Happiness be small, busy and eight-legged
for a couple of years –
Unhappiness, step out of my house,
go back to the wilderness,
where I can't hear the rustle of your black weeds
or even the shadow of your sobs

Now, raise your game, Happiness,
slip off your spider costume,
come to me in the shape of a wren
weaving your common or garden nest –

I don't ask for an outbreak of joy so major
the police are called to quell it,
just your wren-song
drawing each no-longer-endless day to a close,
chanteuse of last light,
such modest happiness I think I can bear

Penelope Shuttle

'When Happiness Returns After a Long Absence' taken from *Sandgrain and Hourglass* published by Bloodaxe Books. Reproduced by permission of David Higham Associates.

"The poem is written from an understanding that happiness can feel a long way off, and even threatening, when someone is going through dark times. The descriptions make it tangible, manageable and even possible but not unrealistic. I find it a very hopeful poem." Gemma Dyson

"... this poem was for me a feeling of being set free. Free from the heavy weight of even breathing, after loss. It held huge respect for the time taken and the journey back to simply functioning again. I couldn't help but think of the family and friends I know who have been walking this path for years themselves." Mel J.

Metaphor describes one thing in terms of another and here the poet describes increasing happiness as an ant, a beetle, then a spider, and eventually, as a wren. Metaphor can often make us see things in a fresh way.

> "But by choosing a spider I felt humbled somehow, like I had never respected the quiet perseverance of that, maybe not so ordinary creature. I could feel the quiet 'slip' from one state to another, happiness allowed to be in view, in earshot, but without a fanfare. Just acceptance that this is how it is." Mel J.

Metaphor is inherently playful and can yield surprising results – often the metaphor that springs to mind is rich in new associations. I suggested to the group that they make a poem, finding their own animal metaphor for happiness. Perhaps you would like to try that too – if your happiness were an animal, what would it be? Make a poem starting with "Let her (or him) be" .... and then later, include the phrase, "Raise your game, happiness ..."

Here are some of the responses from the Truro group:

> "I felt that my response was rather naive but nevertheless quite sweet; prayer-like:
>
> When happiness returns
> Let her be a buzzing bee
> Buzzing from one delicate bud
> To the next
> Transferring the pollen of joy
> From one to another....
>
> Now raise your game, Happiness
> Fly into my heart ...
> Keep me connected to others and
> Help me to be generous with your honey."
>
> Ruth Hausmann
>
> "... Let my puppy chew up unhappy thoughts,
> Anxious thoughts,
> Angry thoughts

And poop them out behind the shed in a
Pile of smelly, steamy mess...

And as the puppy grows,
My happiness grows,
And grows, and grows, and grows –
Golden and glorious and goofy:
Rolling in the mud and the weeds,
Chewing up everything life throws at me."

Gemma Dyson

When working in health and social care, there is inevitably sadness and loss. Poetry, art, music and the natural world have the potential to lift the spirits and remind us that it's possible to find joy even if in difficult and challenging times.

"I've often thought that one of the main reasons people keep pets is because they can give us a vision of complete and unalloyed happiness, which is something that humans very rarely achieve. They remind us of that possibility...

Let him be a cat
weaving himself through my legs in the hall,
stretched horizontal along the sofa top,
squirrelling straight up a tree trunk
just to show that he can,
curled around my feet so that I feel
his purring in my toes.

How can a happy cat raise his game?
He can't, because he's at the top of it already
and unworried by upstarts –
so why should he try?
They say you can never be fully happy
if you know there are others better off than you.
A purring cat does not know this,
or knows that there are not,
or doesn't care."

Tom Scott

"I thought this was a great way to end the session, very positive, uplifting and fun! Obviously in a therapeutic setting, it is important to gauge the needs of the group, but I think it is good to provide some balance and for people to have the opportunity for fun even in the midst of more difficult emotions. I also imagine that at the end of a group, where members may have opened up some powerful feelings, something a little lighter and more optimistic to prepare them to rejoin the 'real world' is a great help."

Gemma Dyson

I now invite you to re-enter the 'real world' and hope that this brief encounter with poetry might inspire you to read and write more of your own.

References

Motion, A. (2009). *The cinder path*. UK: Faber & Faber.

Shuttle, P. (2010). *Sandgrain and hourglass*. Northumberland, UK: Bloodaxe Books.

A Handful of Stones by Geraldine Green
For Marilyn

She stands wide, legs
  apart, arms raised

fists shaking she
  makes faces

at the sun, bends
  down

collects pebbles
  from the shore

tucks each one inside
  her blouse

she has five nestled
  there - maybe more -

she imagines they'll
  hatch into baby birds

grow wings
  fly across oceans

the tide
  creeps in

she stands wide
  shakes fists

inside her blouse
  - warm as figs

nestles a handful
  of stones.

Chapter 5 – Writing the Road to Recovery

Lisa Rossetti

"We are right to have faith in the power of writing and the therapeutic benefits of journal writing." (Thompson, 2010, p. 214)

I began journaling on 3 March 2009, and continue to this day to write in my journal notebooks every morning.

The following account is very much a personal record of how I used journal writing to cope with the depression brought on by hyperthyroidism. Nonetheless, I hope that this chapter will provide a useful introduction to journaling for anyone facing their own difficult times. I trust it will also be of interest for professionals working in health and social care settings.

For those interested in the science behind journal writing for therapeutic purposes, I have included a brief paragraph towards the end of this chapter, as well as some useful links and references.

Journal writing today

Keeping a journal or diary as a therapeutic aid for personal growth started to become popular in the twentieth century. Both Jung and Freud encouraged their patients to record their dreams in writing. Prominent contemporary figures, such as Dr Ira Progoff and Dr James Pennebaker (Progoff, 1977; Pennebaker, 1997), have conducted studies into the therapeutic benefits of journal writing. Author and psychotherapist, Kathleen Adams (Adams, 1990; Adams, 2012) founded the Center for Journal Therapy in 1988, offering workshops for people interested in journal writing for both personal and professional development.

Therapeutic and creative writers Kate Thompson and Gillie Bolton (Thompson, 2010; Bolton, 1999), among others have published several books exploring the practice and benefits of writing in journals. American authors Julia Cameron and Christina Baldwin (Cameron, 2011; Baldwin, 1977), have also contributed to popularising journal writing for personal growth.

Beginning my journey

Initially, I started to journal for personal and professional development. My coaching supervisor recommended Julia Cameron's self-help book, *The Artist's Way* (Cameron, 2011), to increase my self-reflection and creativity in my work as a coach.

However, there are more personal reasons why I wholeheartedly recommend the practice of journal writing. During a period of ill health, I found that journaling gave me a simple and effective way to cope with anxiety and depression. My thoughts and feelings were in turmoil during this difficult time, and I found journaling helped me to make sense of my situation. Journaling helped me to identify and sometimes challenge my negative self-talk and unhelpful behaviours.

A journal is a place where you can come to know and accept yourself, just as you are without censure (although I discovered that I had an inner critic or 'inner policeman' who seemed ever present!). I found writing in my journal, as Julia Cameron (Cameron, 2011, p. 15) says, to be "a pathway to a strong and clear sense of self."

My first steps

In January 2008, I was diagnosed as having a 'massive attack' of my thyroid gland. I had been feeling increasingly and profoundly tired for about six months, so this came as no surprise. I had all the typical symptoms of hypothyroidism: rapid and relentless weight gain, exhaustion and depression.

Looking in the mirror, I hardly recognised myself: coarse hair, swollen throat and 'moon face'. It became a huge challenge for me just to take a small flight of stairs. The simplest act of paying a bill became a monumental mental effort. I had to have assistance taking off my coat because my muscles were so weak.

Around the same time, my work situation was becoming increasingly stressful. I was facing a possible redundancy and an uncertain future. I began to experience episodes of acute anxiety, especially in the middle of the night.

Journaling helped me to come to terms with what was happening in my life mentally and physically when events felt increasingly out of my control. The task of writing three pages each morning was sometimes the only thing that I could accomplish in my day; that, at least, was achievable.

Journaling was not the only method of dealing with anxiety and depression that I tried. I sought help from a hypnotherapist, and listened to CDs on relaxation. These practices helped to some extent, but for me journaling was more effective, helping me to discover and nurture inner resources.

Moreover, the act of writing everyday without inner censure began to gradually release my buried creativity. I was rediscovering myself, and beginning to acknowledge aspects of my personality that I had not expressed for many years.

Continuing the journey

A consistent theme throughout my journals is self-discovery and life choices. I wrote on the first page of my journal *I am experiencing a deeply unacknowledged sorrow ... a feeling of not choosing what is right for* me.

My journal became a place to ask many questions. I didn't expect answers to come out of the blue. By asking questions in my journal, I seemed to set in motion a process of self-enquiry. In this way, journaling improved my self-determination and motivation, which had been so undermined by my illness.

I wrote in bed (and still do) as soon as I woke up. Writing my three pages every morning soon became a comforting routine. I often wrote about what I heard and saw first thing in the morning, sounds in the street, sunbeams on the wall, cloud patterns glimpsed through the window. This seemed to have a calming effect; I remember feeling profoundly reassured by this new rhythm of waking and writing.

In Gillie Bolton's book: *The Therapeutic Potential of Creative Writing* (Bolton, 1999), she describes journal writing as cathartic, a haven, and a friend. I also felt that my own journal did somehow seem 'interested' in what I was about to write. I was 'meeting myself on the page'.

However, I also felt quite self-conscious at first, especially because my husband kept asking me what I was writing, or wanting to chat when I wanted to write.

My first journals are full of 'swirling thoughts', abstractions, emotional outbursts, as well as some quite profound insights into my mental processes and recognitions of negative behaviour patterns. Daily journaling introduced a sense of coherence.

Understandably, much of my early writing deals with my worsening physical condition and quality of life. There are daily references to insomnia, and some moments of real despair. But there are also moments of extraordinary beauty, descriptions of nature and friendship.

Journal extract: 31 March 2009: *I am reluctant to start writing for fear of the moans and groans that will come out. I am exhausted and cannot find myself anywhere.*

An extract written on 1 May 2009: *I am very tired this morning but the brain is whirring about. Sometimes it just looks for problems to solve.*

A few weeks later, I wrote: *I am more composed and quiet, but a bit scared of the journey ahead.*

I also used my journal to plan my day, make lists, and set goals. As my health improved, so my motivation returned and I was able to move forward with some of my plans. My journal writing was really helpful to encourage me to make little steps, and to acknowledge my progress.

Another journal extract from 10 April 2009: *The idea of small change consistently plus 'OK for today' [an affirmation] is a good one. The practice [of journaling] is good, feels absolutely right.*

Learning and discovering

The therapeutic benefits of journaling are many. You will discover your own. Personally, I found the benefits of journaling to be:

- A place to meet myself and learn to become my own friend and advisor.

- A record of my inner feelings which I could revisit and reflect on at a later date.

- A non-threatening and entirely private place to release feelings and tensions.

- A simple way to refocus my energies on what is important to me.

- Rediscovering my own path and taking responsibility for it again.

- An encouraging reminder of my recovery and personal growth.

Starting your own journal

"How do I get started?" This is a frequent question when I suggest journaling to others. Writing in your journal is not the same as setting out to write your memoirs or a novel (although it may be a rich source of material later on). Journaling is basically a very simple activity, with no mastery of writing techniques or perfect spelling needed. It is a misconception to think that all journal writers must be 'creative souls'. You can keep a journal even if you have never written anything in your life before.

As Gillie Bolton says, whatever you write is not wrong (Bolton, 1999, p.120), so spelling, grammar, punctuation and the like are not in the least important. What is important is that you write and write regularly. The pages become a kind of oasis or sanctuary where you can meet yourself on the page.

Julia Cameron (2011) recommends writing three pages (she does not stipulate the number of words or the size of page) as a discipline on a daily basis. She calls these the 'Morning Pages'.

But the blank page can be both an invitation and a daunting place at times. People often ask me "What do you write about?" You do not need to decide what to write. You can simply start with where you are in the moment. What needs to be written will emerge, if you let it. You will find a hidden magic in your pen or pencil!

Like any new activity, whether ten minutes of yoga in the morning or a morning run, it takes repetition to incorporate journaling into your regular routine. Objections start surfacing almost immediately, "I haven't got time." Yet to write three small pages a day takes no more than ten minutes of quiet time.

Set aside 10 to 15 minutes; in the morning if that suits you. Write in a quiet and comfortable place. I write in bed early in the morning. You may prefer to sit in your favourite chair or in a home office as long as this is not distracting. Journal writing is not 'homework', so choose whatever environment supports you to simply write.

Tools and materials

The beauty of journaling is that you don't need to learn any new skills. The equipment is simple and inexpensive, a notebook and a pen or pencil. I personally recommend the good old-fashioned activity of writing on paper rather than keyboarding. It is soothing, and away from your computer you do not have the added distractions of emails and so forth.

Choose a simple A4 or A5 notebook in which you will be happy to write, but not so beautiful that you dare not sully its pages. Well meaning friends have given me lovely notebooks as presents in the past and they remain on my shelves with virgin pages. I buy lined A5 notebooks from my local pound-stretcher store at around £2.99. It is helpful to have a journal of a handy size to keep near your bedside or chosen writing place.

Reviewing your journal

Reviewing what you have written can be both enlightening and reassuring. It would be easy to feel guilty about the burden that I placed on my husband during those difficult times. However, revisiting these pages some two and a half years later I have discovered myself to be a brave woman, struggling to find a new identity and meeting tough personal challenges. My journal reveals a degree of courage that I have rarely acknowledged in myself.

I recommend leaving what you've written unread for several weeks. You may need to first get comfortable with the flow of uncensored writing, as well as establish the practice of writing every day. After say six weeks, you may like to review what you have written in your journals.

Approach your notebooks with compassion and curiosity. Don't judge your thoughts or your writing; ignore punctuation, spelling, and grammar.

One way to review your writing is to choose a quiet place and time. Then simply read what you have written. You can read chronologically or dip in at random. Now that I have been journaling for a few years, I sometimes use 'On This Day', i.e., revisiting the same date from a past year. Absorb what you find on the page; you are meeting yourself. You might like to use a highlighter pen to underline anything that strikes you as particularly interesting.

Why journal writing works

My personal experience was that journal writing helped to calm my anxieties and feel more in control of my emotions. I felt that writing was helping my body get physically better too. But why did this work for me? Here are two scientific explanations from recent research.

Researchers from the University of California (Lieberman, 2007; Wolpert, 2007) have discovered that writing and naming emotions have a calming effect on the brain. Writing reduces activity in the amygdala, the almond-shaped part of the brain connected with anxiety and distress, that drives our 'Flight and Fight' behaviours. Writing, say the researchers, increases activity in the prefrontal cortex, the mind's regulator, thus calming mental activity and emotions.

Dr Pennebaker (1997) has also conducted studies into writing for health, especially around difficult emotions. He found that the release offered by just twenty minutes of writing boosted the immune function, improving its ability to withstand stress and ward off disease.

Conclusion

Recovery is a very personal process; it takes as long as it does, and it may be slow. It is often described as a journey, involving personal development and change. The daily practice of journaling can help you to begin that journey, accepting that life brings problems to be faced. You will discover your own strengths that may have been hidden for some time. You will start generating new possibilities for yourself. In this way, we begin to take control over our own lives, and start to cultivate hope and foster positive change.

For me, out of much adversity came personal development and growth. Journaling helped me to change my perception of myself and strengthened my inner resources. It was an important tool in my recovery; and I continue to 'write the road'.

References

Adams, K. (1990). *Journal to the self: Twenty-two paths to personal growth*. New York: Grand Central Publishing.

Adams, K. (2012). *Center for journal therapy*. Retrieved 8 March 2012 from http://www.journaltherapy.com/

Baldwin, C. (1977). *One to one: Self-understanding through journal writing*. New York: M. Evans.

Bolton, G. (1999). *The therapeutic potential of creative writing: Writing myself*. London: Jessica Kingsley.

Cameron, J. (2011) *The artist's way: A course in discovering and recovering your creative self* (7th ed.). London: Pan.

Lieberman, (2007). Putting feelings into words: Affect labeling disrupts amygdala activity in response to affective stimuli. *Psychological Science*, 18(5), 421-428.

Pennebaker, J. W. (1997). Writing about emotional experiences as a therapeutic process. *Psychological Science*, 8(3), 162-166.

Progoff, I. (1977). *At a journal workshop: The basic text and guide for using the intensive journal.* Oxford: Dialogue House Library.

Thompson, K. (2010) *Therapeutic journal writing: An introduction for professionals.* London: Jessica Kingsley.

Wolpert, S. (2007). *Putting feelings into words produces therapeutic effects in the brain.* Retrieved 8 March 2012 from http://www.universityofcalifornia.edu/news/article/9305

Relapse by Lorraine Gibbard

I know this place
I've been here before
The clutter of lives
Breaking my strength.

No one hears my silent scream
Few perceive my pain
I struggle to hold my life in balance
The threads of the web are too taught.

There is nothing I can do
The pieces of my life disintegrate
I call out as I free fall down

"what can I hold onto, where is my fixing point?"
And Jesus replies, "You hold onto me".
His hand grasps mine and I cling to his.
Healing begins again.

Freezing You Out by Carol Ross

I found
a moody young river
angrily churning
past ice-fringed rocks.

I sent
the confetti of your letters
swirling downstream
into soggy oblivion.

I wept
in the tangled roots
of an old willow
until all my tears dried.

I dropped
your memory in the black water
and saw it freeze
like your frozen heart.

I marvelled
as the glinting current
twisted my thoughts
towards recovery.

Moods by Steve Childerley

When I feel a bit low, with no get up and go,
I sit down and write a few verses.
It helps clear my mind and relax and unwind,
And feel good as my low mood disperses.

In my mind, as I write, my mood gathers height,
As I drift along mountain and moor,
Through The Lakes, to the coast, with the views I love most.
I describe all the scenes I adore.

Then I make them all rhyme, it may take me some time,
And I live my trip to the full.
I can go where I like on my 'virtual' hike,
I feel good, I no longer feel dull.

Moving On (Patricia Jackson)

Writing a journal at times can be a pain
But looking back over it there is much to gain
What is written in there is honest and true
A record of feelings, some happy, some blue

Exploring the past no doubt can be frightening
But realisations we come to can be so enlightening
Peaks, troughs, fear and yes some tears
Allow us to move on over the years.

Moving forward accept it's good to be truthful
At the same time, liberating, disconcerting and sometimes painful
Fear of failure often stops us from trying
But not to try is a failure we can hear ourselves crying

Expectations we place on ourselves feel simplistic
On reflection however, some are quite unrealistic
Accepting that perfection in all is quite unattainable
Enables our emotions and actions to become more sustainable

Valuing ourselves and looking to our core
Trusting our instincts and values, why do we look for more
All our actions, thoughts and deeds are truly part of you and me
We should all stand strong and proud, there for all to see

Sometimes we're happy to stay within our comfort zone
Risky business stepping out of this, perhaps feeling alone
But stepping forward to accept whatever comes our way
To take a risk, embrace new things, surely a small price to pay

Past experiences can arouse painful feedback
But away in a suitcase prepare this ready to pack
And move on with life and accept each day
That our journey will take us on its own special way

Life moves so quickly, that's plain to see
But it's really okay, sometimes to 'just be'

Chapter 6 – Rebuilding My Life Through Writing
Katie Metcalfe

"I am, I am, I am." Plath (2005)

I am a writer, publisher, poet, editor and survivor. I have a long history of mental illness that started when I was 14, and going through a great time of stress and anxiety in my life. I desired control and clarity, rather than the daily difficulties at home and school. I stopped eating properly and started to exercise obsessively, living by the rules of a voice in my head. I quickly developed anorexia nervosa. Instead of achieving control and clarity, my life was pulled apart at the seams in a matter of months. I was unable to concentrate, on *anything*. My brain was dry, my body lacking the nourishment it needed to function properly. I couldn't talk to my family without arguing. I couldn't eat around people. I couldn't sit still. I couldn't get warm. I couldn't laugh, smile or have fun. If I disobeyed my illness I got 'fat.' Around the same time all of this kicked off, I developed manic depression. Any part of me that was stitched back together, through loving words and caring family and friends, was quickly torn apart again. Aged 15, I was admitted into a psychiatric hospital, weighing a meagre five and a half stone. I still believed I was overweight. I thought if I couldn't maintain my routine, there was no point living. But *something* kept me going. That something was writing. Every day was a struggle. I kept diaries, logging everything that went on, in neat, gothic script, including everything I ate and drank, right down to the last spoonful of soup and 250 millilitres of water. I agree with Gillie Bolton, a consultant in therapeutic writing, who says "A diary is written for its own sake, for the joy, the painful release, the discovery, the ordering and making sense, the creation, the re-experiencing, the reaffirmation of the self." (Bolton, 1998, p.30). Writing seemed the natural thing to do. Words gave me power, and helped me to feel like I was taking control. At first, I was blind to what I was writing. The reality of my condition didn't dawn on me, until five months down the line, because it, the illness, had become ordinary. I realised what I was doing would kill me before long. I *had to* change my life.

Writing helped me cope with bad thoughts and powerful emotions, in a constructive way, now I had this drive to get better. I was able to write through my anger and stress. It was much more beneficial than refusing to eat or having an argument. I would often write down how I felt and give it to my family to read. Trying to vocalise issues wasn't my strong point. Things always seemed to come out wrong. When you're speaking, you don't have a second chance. You say it and it's out there. With writing, you can edit and re-draft as many times as you like to make your writing say exactly what you want it to.

Writing took on the very important role of therapy, and accompanied me on my journey to recovery. "The word 'journal' comes from the French journee: day. Journal –journee –journey: The word contains both continuity and change, temporal and geographical, with direction and movement ... This becomes a powerful metaphor for the relationship between person and life. A journal is a journey, a way of finding a voice." (Philips, Penman & Linnington, 1999, p.73).   After five months on bedrest I'd accumulated enough material to start writing a book about my experiences. I wanted to try and help other people in a similar situation, who didn't know which way to turn. But there was one real problem. How could I write a book about recovering from anorexia, when I wasn't trying as hard as I could to recover myself? I'd made a breakthrough in my recovery, finding my true passion, my meaning for life, but there was a lot of really hard work ahead of me. Rainer Maria Rilke expresses the challenge perfectly. "A work of art is good if it has grown out of necessity." (R. M. Rilke, cited in Angwin 2005, p.13).

"When we just let ourselves write, we get it right." (Cameron, 2000, p.2).

Recovering from anorexia took many years. I relapsed more times than I can remember, but writing pulled me back from the brink of being re-admitted into hospital. I started college and began to get involved in literary events, meeting new writers, whose lives were governed by their passion for the written word. I made the effort to try new things, to diversify and explore new areas of writing, which helped massively in increasing my confidence and making me feel better about myself, not only as a writer, but as a human being.

When I performed my poetry for the first time at an open mic event, I felt as if a light switch had been flicked on. Performing once a month or so opened me up to new opportunities, and gave me a goal to work towards which didn't involve food or weight. This helped focus my mind. I really felt as though I was part of something important to me. I was able to keep calm about things that would have previously upset me. I was thinking deeper and appreciating life much more.

I became involved with a magazine called KENAZ created by North East writers Bob Beagrie and Andy Willoughby. It's often full of hard hitting subjects such as breakdowns, eating disorders and substance abuse. They published my first piece of writing *Healing through creative writing.* When I'd have down days, I would read the first paragraph to myself, *'Writing has the power to heal the human mind, body and soul. Writing can pull you from the depth of depression. Writing can save lives; I know that it most certainly saved mine.'* (Metcalfe, 2006a, p.29).

Through writing and having work published, I conquered hurdles impossible to overcome with psychiatrists who didn't really understand me. I've learnt other important lessons too:

- Break routines
- Practise ignoring negative thoughts
- Be happy now

Despite contrary beliefs, recovering from anorexia does *not* just include eating and gaining weight. It is *vital* to change thinking patterns. Creative visualisation: using mental imagery and affirmation to produce positive changes in your life, played a huge role in helping me achieve my goals. I'd visualise my book on a shelf many times a day. Before the year was out, my book was published! I'm not saying visualisation works miracles, you have to put the hard work in, but it assists you massively in achieving your goals, and you can use it for any aspect of your life.

I found by writing about my experiences, I was able to see my illness from a different perspective. I was able to focus on where I was going wrong and what I needed to do to improve my situation. My primary method of recovery was writing through my problems. When my first book *Anorexia: A stranger in the Family* came out (Metcalfe, 2006b), I realised it was perhaps one of the best things I have done in my life, and it encouraged me to stay well.

I'm now fully recovered from anorexia nervosa and write every day. My book is in libraries across the country. I've given talks in schools and *Anorexia: A stranger in the Family* has been adapted into a play to educate young people on the dangers of eating disorders. In my recovery, writing was as essential as eating. In my ongoing battle with manic depression, writing is as crucial as taking my medication. I cannot stress enough the importance of creativity if you are involved with mental health in any way. No matter what you want from your writing it can provide for you, so long as you make the time and effort to feed into it. If you are too shy to call yourself a writer, remember: you become what you practise most.

"A piece of paper and a pen is nearly always available, unlike the doctor or counsellor, like having a private therapist day and night." (Bolton, 1998, p.23)

Writing is the best thing that's ever happened to me. I live to write. Nothing makes me happier. I can be feeling low, worthless and sad, but writing *always* pulls me back. Nevertheless, as poet Bob Beagrie says "it is important to recognise that creative writing provides a highly effective tool for personal development but is certainly not a 'cure all' and is too often used as a tokenistic band-aid upon a gaping wound." (Beagrie, 2011). This is where support from family, friends and health workers comes in. The best piece of advice I can give is to write from the heart. Don't think about anyone else. This is *your* thing. Writing is, without a doubt, a much underused therapy, as Jim Pollard for the Guardian explains.

"If it were a drug, this versatile little treatment would surely have a public profile to match Viagra. Indeed, the lack of a pharmaceutical company to promote it is perhaps part of the reason why its benefits are so little known. It's cheaper than any drug – the cost of a pen and paper." (Pollard, 2002).

Practical tips

Ensure you have reliable support: If you're writing about your health or the health of someone else, make sure you have support. Emotions can increase when you are writing about sensitive issues, making you feel vulnerable. So it's always good to have someone you can talk to.

Buy a notebook and diary: A notebook is essential for a writer. "Your notebook is for you, and it needs to contain whatever helps you or fuels your writing." (Anderson, 2005, p.33). It's crucial to be happy with it. I always choose an A5, black, unlined notebook. It's easy to carry around and with blank pages, I don't feel restricted. It needs to be something you can write in. Sounds silly, but if you can't stand the thought of making a mess of a gorgeous notebook, it isn't for you. Settle for a 99p one. Write anything and everything, from an overheard conversation to the colour of the autumn leaf stuck to your shoe with bubble gum. Carrying your notebook around with you is an excellent reminder to yourself that you *are* a writer, when everything else seems to be taking over. Regarding diaries, I like them to be blank, so I'm not restricted by dates, lines and page size. A diary is such a personal thing, but also something I believe is crucial in your development as a writer.

Pens: I'm addicted to stationery. I drool over Parker fountain pens. I've grown to adore Paper Mate Stick 2020 with black ink. Tough, reliable and they take ages to stop working.

Don't worry: Forget about grammar, punctuation, spelling and all that jazz. What is most important is *you* getting *your* words out and onto the page. Think about the other stuff later.

Doing your best and moving forward: Do your best in what you do and move on. Don't go over and over the same piece, trying to 'perfect' it. There's no such thing. Just write, write, and write some more. You can always come back to things. There's nothing better than that feeling of pride when you have finished a piece of writing, and the anticipation of starting something new.

Exercises

When you are working through these exercises, use your five senses. This helps make the piece more vivid, and draws the reader in. Use as much detail as possible. Talk about the colour of your shirt or the hot, sticky weather. When you start writing about life events, you can have all sorts of recollections. Dialogue can help to make a piece feel alive and realistic.

Therapeutic writing can assist in your personal growth, self-esteem, career and education, creative self-expression and lifestyle, so it's well worth taking a shot at these exercises. I like to let my inhibitions go and write. I don't write too carefully or try too hard. Don't worry if you go off on a tangent: they can be very revealing and fascinating!

Memories and thoughts

Freewrite

Write for 10 minutes, every day, without stopping to look back over what you've written. This helps you loosen up, write more easily and reveal creative ideas and valuable thoughts.

Journey

We all make journeys every day and think nothing of it because we believe it is generally a 'mundane' activity. I'd like you to focus on a journey you have taken and write about it. You might become aware of things you've never noticed before.

1. Where was your starting point? Can you describe it in detail?
2. What transport did you use? Why?
3. Did you travel with anyone? Why were you travelling with them?
4. What were the travelling conditions like? How did they make you feel?
5. Where was your destination? What did you do when you arrived?

An important day

Important days make and break us. Write about one of yours.

1. Can you name an important day and why it was significant?
2. What did you do on this day?
3. How did you feel emotionally, physically, mentally?
4. Who was with you?
5. Who would you have wanted to be there?
6. What were the highpoints and low points? What would you have changed?
7. What did you take away from this day? How did you feel when it ended?

Clothing

Our clothing says a lot about us as people. Again, clothes are often overlooked. Think and write about yours for a while. I'm sure some interesting things will creep out from the stitches and stains.

1. What is your favourite piece of clothing? What does it look like?

2. Why is it your favourite piece over others?

3. What do you feel like when you wear it?

4. Where did it come from?

5. What do other people think of it?

6. What does it say about you as a person?

An important place

Important places stay in our minds for life. Write about yours, using lots of detail and feeling.

1. Where is this place? Describe it.

2. Why is it significant to you?

3. How do you feel when you're there? Why do you feel like this?

4. How do you feel when you need to leave?

Person

We know a lot more about people than we think we do.

1. Name an important person in your life and why they're important.

2. What do they look like? What colour is their hair/eyes?

3. What is their greatest fear?

4. What are their priorities?

5. If granted one wish, what would it be?

Opening up and moving on

These exercises will help you to look, with a positive mind, to the future. During my recovery, exercises like these made sense of the chaos in my head. They were self-revealing, and helped me reflect on personal strengths and achievements, something so crucial in the management of mental health. "When one comes out of a period of depression, the relief is so wonderful, the world, the everyday, ordinary, humdrum world, is so vivid and warm and re-assuring that you see it with a poetic vision and notice, with delight, so many little things that it is so easy to overlook." (Roy Blackman cited in Bolton, 1998, p.218).

Your achievements

1. Think of an achievement. It can be recent or in the past.
2. What was this achievement? Can you describe it in detail?
3. Where did it happen?
4. What made you want to do it?
5. What was the most difficult part and why?
6. How do you feel now, thinking back about it?

Your future

1. Where can you see yourself in five years?
2. Can you describe what you are doing then?
3. What do you look like? What is your health like? How do you feel mentally and emotionally?
4. How will you get to this place and position? Do you have any strategies?
5. How do you feel about it? Does it seem manageable or scary?

Setting yourself goals

Setting goals can motivate you, help you move forward and establish a regular writing routine. Everyone is different when it comes to setting goals. My personal preference is word count. If you're not achieving, ask yourself why. Don't set yourself a target that's too high. Set yourself small, manageable goals and review your progress regularly. I like to make daily, weekly, monthly and yearly goals, which help me structure my writing time.

Diary

Keep a diary for a week, writing in it at least once a day. Keeping a diary is excellent for self exploration, expressing ideas and to organise and clarify thinking. Read back your entries at the end of the week and see if they reveal anything to you. It would be useful and therapeutic to carry on after the week. You will find a bond growing before long, as you start to express thoughts and feelings, ideas and motivations. It will become like a best friend that's always there for you.

Write a letter to your illness as its friend and enemy

This is an excellent opportunity to get issues off your chest, when your therapist is unavailable at 3 am, or you are having a blip during lunch. First of all, write a letter to your illness or whatever is bothering you as its friend. Write down everything that comes to mind. Next, write to it as its enemy. Write everything that you hate about it, how it is affecting your life and how you can do so much better without it. This is an extremely cathartic experience, especially when you rip them up at the end and bin them.

Perhaps the most important thing you can take away from this chapter is the knowledge that writing can help you to take control of your own life, if you just let it.

References

Anderson, L. (2005). *Creative writing: A workbook with readings.* Abingdon, UK: Routledge.

Angwin, R. (2005). *Writing the bright moment: Inspiration and guidance for writers.* UK: Fire in the Head.

Beagrie, B. (2011). *Bob Beagrie.* Retrieved 23 May 2011 from http://www.facebook.com/bob.beagrie

Bolton, G. (1998). *The therapeutic potential of creative writing: Writing myself.* London: Jessica Kingsley.

Cameron, J. (2000). *The Right to Write: An invitation and initiation into the writing life.* London: Sidgwick & Jackson.

Metcalfe, K. (2006a). Healing through creative writing. *KENAZ,* issue 4.

Metcalfe, K. (2006b). *Anorexia: A stranger in the family.* UK: Accent Press.

Philips, D., Penman, D., Linnington, L. (Eds.) (1999). *Writing well: Creative writing and mental health*. London: Jessica Kingsley.

Plath, S. (2005). *The bell jar*. London: Faber and Faber.

Pollard, J. (2002, July 28). *As easy as ABC (The Guardian)*. Retrieved 19 May 2011 from http://www.guardian.co.uk/lifeandstyle/2002/jul/28/shopping

Recommended reading

Astley, N. (2006). *Staying alive*. Northumberland, UK: Bloodaxe Books.

Bolton, G., Howlet, S., Lago, C., Wright, J. (Eds.). (2004) *Writing cures: An introductory handbook of writing in counselling and therapy*. Hove: Brunner-Routledge.

Chambers, A. (2005). *This is all*. London: Bodley Head Children's Books.

Griffiths, J. (2008). *Wild*. London: Penguin.

Gawain, S. (2002). *Creative visualization*. Novato CA: Nataraj Publishing.

Lewis, G. (2006). *Sunbathing in the rain*. London: Harper Perennial.

Metcalfe, K. (2010). *One of many knots*. Middlesbrough: Mudfog.

Tailor Made by Ann Wilson

I will tailor this to your needs
Darn all night
Pick up a thousand dropped threads until
my hands are worn, but you
need to choose the fabric, show me
where to stitch your lining.

After Midday by Sylvia Stevens

Is it enough
to sit
and see the sun
sizzle
the capturing clouds,
look, as the light
ignites the moss
to emerald fire,
feel the wind
feather-flirt
with the giggling grasses,
in the shade-dapples
green-growing afternoon?

Is it enough
to hear
the hustle
of high blown branches,
smell the star-shine on the sap
in the pine shade,
glimpse gleaming wings
as they circle and shadow,
in the jade-dappled
green-glowing afternoon?

Hope by Leona Byers

I'm only 15 years old; to me anorexia is new;
I've never come across the beast, and now i don't know what to do.
Many people suffer, from the illness that lies deep inside,
I am the girl who knows it all, all the feelings you try to hide.
As time has passed, my weight is falling;
But i will not be taken by the voice that is calling.
She stands before me, making me fear –
But please do trust me, my precious dear,
For i am the girl who understands,
I know of the struggle and the persistent demands.
I know the urge to purge and fast,
But to be defeated by the beast is the thing I'll do last.
With friends and family supporting you all the way;
Take my word, as i promise it will all be okay.
A fighter my self i know all too well,
How life can feel like a living hell.
But she has not won, and that she will not...
Anorexia is the disease that i have got.
Recovery is the progress that i shall make –
From this darkened nightmare, we shall awake.
For every illness there is a cure,
We can all pull through this, of that I'm sure.
So don't you think that no one will understand;
My dearest friend i offer my hand.
When ever you feel trapped and unsure of what to do,
Remember that you are strong, and that you can pull through.
And when ever you feel that you can not cope,
Just remember, dear friend, that there is HOPE.

Working as a Journalist by Julia Clifford

I love doing my writing and I find it really therapeutic. I feel that I have been really lucky in that many mental health professionals, who have been involved in my care, have given me considerable support in helping me develop my literary skills.

Some seven and a half years ago I set up my own magazine and much to my agreeable surprise it has genuinely proved to be quite successful. I have now built up quite a loyal readership. Many of my friends, my family, the people from Church and some of the volunteers from Mind have become my regular customers. I charge a small fee for the majority of my publications. Although I like to think that I am running a business my care co-ordinators have told me that in reality I am just recouping my own costs. It is all done through self-publication and I rely totally on my own PC and printer in order to produce my own magazines.

I write under a pseudonym. I use the same pseudonym for all of my magazines. I regard this pseudonym as my alter-ego. In my own mind she has an identity that is an extension of my own personality. I regard her as the self confident and efficient part of myself.

Chapter 7 – Writing Together: Therapeutic Writing in Mental Health

Part 1 – *Reflections of a Writing Practitioner*

Carol Ross

Have you ever thrown yourself into something and then just when it's too late to draw back, you panic? That's how I felt when I started a weekly writing group for patients in a mental health unit as part of the Cumbria Partnership Year of Writing (see Chapter 12). I was motivated to start the sessions both by my own personal experience of the enjoyment and therapy that writing can bring, and by the large amount of research evidence I had been reading that shows writing can be of therapeutic benefit – both psychologically and physically (see Chapter 1). But I was nervous – would I enjoy the sessions or hate them? Did I have the right skills? Would the patients gain any benefit? Fortunately the answers to those questions were: yes I loved doing the sessions from the beginning; yes I had prepared enough beforehand so that my skills were up to the job (but I am still learning all the time); and yes patients do seem to gain benefit from participating in the sessions (an evaluation of the 2010 sessions and of other Year of Writing workshops has been published, see Ross, 2011).

At the time of writing I am leading weekly groups in the mental health unit in which I started in April 2010, and in a psychiatric intensive care unit. In my writing groups I do not feel like a therapist or a teacher (I am neither), I feel I just sit down with some people, we get to know each other a little, and we write together. I believe that writing does you good, whatever you write, but that different people need to write different things and in different styles, e.g., thoughts and feelings, memories, imaginative stories, poems. What I aim to do is help people to discover what they need (or want) to write and inspire them to keep writing – and they inspire me right back!

Getting ready

I felt I needed to prepare really well before starting to lead sessions, which I did by:

- Reading books and research articles
- Attending training, e.g., psychological skills training and certificates in counselling and creative writing
- Planning meetings with ward management, clinical psychologist, nurse consultant, occupational therapist and activities coordinator
- Identifying a senior clinician willing to supervise my practice
- Going through the Lapidus Core Competencies (Flint, Hamilton & Williamson, 2004) with my supervisor to ensure I have no competency gaps
- Identifying an evaluation tool (Stiles, Gordon & Lani, 2002) for the pilot writing sessions and adapting it in consultation with ward management.

A typical session

Recruitment of inpatients to attend the group is by a combination of posters advertising the sessions, discussion with ward staff and visiting the communal areas just before the session to ask who would like to join in.

I bring pens and paper along to each session, a supply of the forms I use (evaluation questionnaire and feedback form), plus whatever stimuli I plan to use – objects, pictures, etc.

Before the session starts I speak to a member of ward staff about who might be interested in coming to the group and either accompany them on a tour of the unit to let people know the group is about to start, or go directly to the activities room to clear art materials and pictures off one of the tables so we have room to write.

The group participants generally arrive over the course of several minutes so I chat with the early arrivals until it seems like everyone is present who plans to be and then start the session.

The first 5 minutes or so of each session are taken up with explaining what the group is about, getting to know each other a little, and reassuring group members, for example: that they are writing only for themselves, that no-one else needs to see anything they write, and that things like spelling, grammar, handwriting and punctuation don't matter at all. Reassurances are important, not least because some people had a bad experience of school and are initially worried that the group might be like school.

I have developed an outline programme for the sessions: introductions, reassurances and explanations; a short writing exercise, e.g., freewriting (see Chapter 1) from 4 prompt words (2 minutes per word); a longer writing exercise; completion of evaluation forms. My writing sessions typically include around 25 minutes of writing and 25-30 minutes of reading aloud (our own writing and sometimes published poems) and group discussion. Participants are under no pressure to read aloud, but in practice almost everyone does at some stage. Feedback suggests that the sharing of writing and the group discussions greatly contribute to the benefit felt by participants.

Depending on the individuals who come to the group, the sessions sometimes extend beyond an hour. The extra time is not used for writing, but rather for chatting over coffee, reading and discussing poetry, talking about ideas for writing, and discussing possible homework and the plan for the next session.

At the request of the ward manager I now write some of my observations in the patients' care records using feedback forms.

The group takes place in the ward activities room, which is a light modern room. We do not have exclusive use of the room for the session, which means other patients do occasionally come in to sit with us for a while or to do an art or craft activity. The activities room is described in the following poem, which was written while I was on a Writing in Healthcare course at Tŷ Newydd, the National Writers' Centre for Wales (Tŷ Newydd, 2012):

Hadrian Writing Group

I am in a light, airy place.
White walls are strewn with coloured shapes,
a stream bed of giant pebbles.
A giant could fold these walls out flat,
make himself a huge abstract painting.

There is a mess of art stuff scattered.
Paint pots and brushes beside a sink.
Pictures and poems on the walls.
A Dolly Mix of plastic chairs huddle
round two white Formica tables.

Our table is near the windows.
Our heads are bowed, eyes downcast.
Our hands are moving, sliding over paper,
pens softly scratching in the hush.

I can hear birdsong,
faraway voices.
My muscles are relaxing,
tensions easing.
Our minds are calming,
creating,
finding flow,
a sense of
connectedness.

Rapport and group dynamics

I believe the success of small group therapeutic creative writing sessions is greatly influenced by how comfortable and supported participants feel in the group, and on the development of confidence to share writing, thoughts and feelings with each other. Writing itself is therapeutic, but writing and sharing writing in a supportive group adds another dimension. For example, some people who had probably never written creatively before, gained confidence within the space of one session, and over several sessions, in response to the heartfelt and supportive feedback they received on their writing from the group.

Rapport between facilitator and participants is vital for creating a relaxed, supportive group. Rapport and good group dynamics can be fostered in many ways, e.g., by being friendly and approachable and using only first names in the group. I try to speak to participants not as their group leader but just as one person to another. I make it a rule to write and read aloud with the group. Sometimes someone is unable or unwilling to write for all sorts of different reasons, e.g., not having learned to read and write, reading glasses left at home, arthritis. Everyone is welcome in my groups and if they don't or can't write on the day in question we find ways of working around it, e.g., when it comes time to read our writing aloud they speak instead, they draw instead, or I write for them. One person wasn't able to write on paper but he was able to compose poems on his phone and read them to us. Everyone needs to feel welcome and valued, which means giving effective reassurances, and encouraging and supportive feedback.

Rationale for selection of writing activities

Writing exercises in mental health wards need to be quite short for two reasons: (i) many of the people who come to the group do not have the concentration needed for a long period of writing while they are ill in hospital, and (ii) some patients arrive late or leave early for all sorts of reasons and having short exercises makes managing this easier. Starting with short bursts of writing, such as freewriting for 2 minutes per word for 4 words, is an easy and calming start and a good 'warm up' for writing.

I select, develop and/or adapt writing activities on the basis of anticipated wellbeing benefits for the participants and suitability for writers of mixed ability and experience. Because there can be new people each week, and the abilities and level of concentration of participants vary, I plan each session as if it were the first session, rather than building on what has gone before. At the same time I need to ensure variety from session to session for the sake of those patients who do attend week on week. A high priority for the selection of writing exercises is always for the sessions to be enjoyable – if people enjoy writing in the session they will hopefully do more writing after the session, both in the unit and after they go home.

Freewriting (see Chapter 1) is a powerful technique for therapeutic creative writing that can draw out unexpected thoughts and feelings. When working in a mental health unit I feel it is helpful to use word prompts or other stimuli for freewriting for these reasons:

(i)   Writing completely freely whatever comes into the mind, with no prompt of any kind, could emphasise any negative thoughts that are in the person's mind at the time of writing, cause distress and make the negative thoughts worse;

(ii)   Writing in small chunks, i.e, 2 minutes per word for 4 words, is an easily manageable start to writing sessions, even for people with a low level of concentration, and avoids a long silence early in the session;

(iii)   Writing from prompt words is less likely to be deeply personal, so the participants are more likely to be willing to read aloud some of what they have written. Reading aloud, sharing thoughts and discussing our writing, seems to contribute to the effects of the writing sessions.

I choose freewriting stimulus words on the basis of (i) avoiding directing participants' thoughts or leading their writing; and (ii) encouraging new thoughts to appear and flow without constraint. For example when the word pool is used one person may write about pool balls rolling around a table while another writes about the moon reflected in a pool of water. Word 'sets' that allow these differences to appear in participants' writing make for interesting group discussions. An alternative approach, with a confident group, is to ask each person, during the introductions at the start of the session, for a word that they associate with wellbeing, and then use those words as freewriting prompts later in the session.

The 15- to 20-minute writing exercises I use include: writing following guided visualizations; journal-writing techniques, and exercises based on weather, places, people, amusing stories, or playing with words. These longer writing exercises are chosen to achieve a balance between opportunities to write in a fun and imaginative way and encouraging writing that is grounded in the here and now, the real world. I take care not to use exercises that will lead participants to write about painful memories and generally do not lead people to write about anything very specific or in a prescribed creative form such as a poem. In this way, participants are free to write what they need or want to write at that moment in time. In one session five people all wrote very differently in a writing exercise about boxes, for example, two of the group wrote rhymed poems while the other three wrote prose.

Inspiration for writing

Here are some examples of writing stimuli that I think can work well in a mental health unit (roughly in the order of frequency that I use them). Where I have quoted from a participant's writing the prompt word or other stimulus is given in square brackets after the quote.

Freewriting, e.g., using sets of words as prompts, e.g., pool, moon, sky and cloud; snow, cave, mountain and river; red, blue, green and yellow.

Graham: "While serving in the Armed Forces an exercise to the Atlas Mountains in Morocco resulted in trekking across peaks early before sunrise. Gentle as a breeze which will only disturb a feather or as strong as a lion with a roar to match." [avalanche]

Carol: "I love it when an avalanche of words pour out of my head onto the page. To me the word avalanche sounds interesting but the things themselves are so destructive and scary." [avalanche]

Graham: "When working I have been described as an animal, what type of animal I do not know but possibly a bull as I am a Taurus." [animal]

The following four pieces of freewriting were all written by the same person (Janice) in a one-to-one writing session. After she had finished writing them I showed her how what she had written could be turned into a poem, which follows the four short pieces.

"Clouds shining in the sky. Birds flying through the air. Black clouds, white clouds. All around clouds." [cloud]

"Sun shining brightly making us happy. Sun mellow yellow brightening the day." [sunshine]

"River flowing past, current flowing fast. Boats and vessels sailing on a blue, clean river. Throwing stones into rivers and splashing." [river]

"Flowing on in chatting. Flowing freely and easily. Flowing on like a river" [river]

On the River with Family and Friends

by Janice and Carol

Clouds shining in the sky
Birds flying through the air
Black clouds, white clouds
Clouds all around.

Sun shining brightly
Making us happy.
Mellow yellow
Sunshine
Brightening the day.

River flowing fast
Current rushing past
Boats and vessels
Sailing on a blue clean
River.

Picture postcards. I use picture postcards often, in all sorts of ways, and consider them to be endlessly adaptable. Often I ask people to each choose a card that appeals and give them ideas to get them started writing, e.g., write what you see, imagine the scene in another season, imagine you were there, write the 'story' of the picture. Sometimes we all write about the same card. Once when I asked everyone to write about the same card and write what they could see in the picture, all but one of us described the tangible elements of the picture – sea, sand, sky, car, man, woman. But interestingly one person wrote solely about the emotions she could see being played out between the man and the woman in the picture. The differences in our responses to the cards and the 'stories' we devise make for interesting writing and stimulating discussions.

George: "I would like to climb up Dodd Fell because it is no longer covered in conifer trees. Perhaps I will see a red squirrel. I have never seen a red squirrel except on posters and in nature magazines. I would like to join the organisation relating to them. I also want to join Friends of the Earth and some similar organisations. This September I am going to start studying for a three-year degree course in Ecology and Environmental Protection at Lancaster University or the University of Cumbria." [a photograph of a red squirrel]

Objects, either an eclectic assortment, e.g., a dolly peg, an evening purse, a compass, a perfume bottle and an ornamental box; or a themed collection, e.g., half a dozen pairs of gloves (including work gloves).

George: "The compass reminds me of wonderful walking days in the Lake District. It also reminds me that I need to buy a compass, and also a rucksack and some waterproof trousers." [a compass]

George: "In the purse there is a pearl. It is a real one. It reminds me of days on the beach." [an empty purse]

Nigel: "Rebecca was excited as she unwrapped the small parcel with which she had just been presented. Inside was a little house. She loved everything miniature and the gift appealed to her enormously. There was ivy growing up the walls and benches outside the front. It was just the sort of perfect little cottage that she imagined living in when she grew up. She wanted to keep a tea shop and this would be ideal. She picked up the house by its roof, which came off, revealing that as well as being a perfect miniature house it was a perfect little box. She knew immediately what she would use it for, she would keep her baby teeth in it. She had just lost her first one and knew that she would keep the rest. The house would make a wonderful place to keep them." [a small box in the shape of a cottage]

Photographs of people, preferably doing something, e.g., sitting outside a café, sleeping, reading, making something. Writing about these can help the writer to look beyond their own life and problems. One way to use photographs of people is for each participant to choose a picture and then write about the person in the picture as if they knew them, which is what the man who wrote this did:

Peter: "My friend's name is Jessica. She has red hair. She is a hairdresser and works all the hours God is prepared to give her. She knows all her customers and they all work for a living. After finishing work she goes to a disco with her female friends and she has a good laugh with her friends. The other day when she was working a woman came in the shop, broke down and cried. She said 'Now that I've wised up I'm not prepared to waste any more years on that horrible husband.' So my friend made her a cup of sweet tea and she calmed down." [a quirky photograph of a young woman with scarlet hair who is holding a magnifying glass to one eye]

Published poems, e.g., we read two different poems aloud; discuss our reactions to them, which we prefer and why; then we each choose one poem, or a line from it, and write something in response.

The following was written in response to "The house is not the same since you left" by Henry Normal (Normal, 1993, p. 21):

Cate: "The poem suggests to me bereavement in the family possibly a man. The cooker is angry suggests that maybe it doesn't get used as much now so it is angry at being left with no work to do. He used to watch the telly especially the football on Saturdays but not now, it stands switched off just catching the sun's reflection from outside. What's the point in washing up for one, who's going to see the dirty pots anyway? The curtains count the days since he last opened them and stood in front of the window. Nothing speaks to me in the house any more, it holds no interest for me know you are gone. The armchair shows your empty space, the space you once took up. The kettle initially constantly on when you first left now stands dormant. No-one comes any more and I can't be bothered. I'm sure the plants will die too once I tell them you have gone. Your mess has gone from the bathroom. How I used to moan about the shaving scum marks around the wash basin and the toilet seat always being up. What I'd give to see that once again. And now it just stays the same and I only need to clean it once a week. The bedroom door stays shut, I just can't face the memories. If I keep it shut then hopefully all the good times and memories will stay inside. But on a night I have to sneak in and weep, the sheets and pillows remind me of you so much. I wish you hadn't gone."

Writing after a guided visualisation. The following two pieces were written after a guided visualisation that started in a garden and ended on a mountain top. I find guided visualisation works best if I don't use a written script when I am guiding the group through the visualisation. I suggest to people they might like to close their eyes during the visualisation part, but I bear in mind that not everyone will feel comfortable doing that. The main drawback to using visualisations is that they take quite a long time to do and a patient who arrives late to the group (as quite often happens) might either interrupt the visualisation and distract the others in the group, or miss it altogether and then not have any inspiration for the writing after the visualisation.

George: "I was in a beautiful garden with a fountain and the birds and butterflies. I walked out of the garden on to a path which led into a wood with oaks and other trees. The path was winding a lot and there was an obstacle on the path. I passed it on the left side and then the path started to slope upwards. It became very steep and then I turned and looked down back where I had come from. The scene was very beautiful. On the path there was someone who looked like Julie. She gave me a bottle of water to drink. The path became very steep and it became apparent that I was climbing a mountain. At the top Auntie Annie was there. I asked her why she was there and she replied that it was to reassure me."

Nigel: "I am sitting by a burn that tumbles down from the hillside, passing under a wall and then winding on downhill. The meadow beyond the wall has just been mown and the smell is wafting toward me. There are roses in the garden, red ones, pink ones and white ones. There are birds singing all around. I get up and walk out of the gate across the meadow to the belt of trees beyond. It has been very windy in the last few days and one tree has blown down across the path. I climb over it and continue uphill. A pretty young woman is coming down the path in hiking boots. She stops at a bend in the path to admire the view, as do I. She proffers chocolate, Cadbury Dairy Milk, which I accept. Neither of us speak, we just stand and look at the view of the valley spread out below. Fortified by chocolate I press on up the hill feeling pain in my knees and pumping in my chest as I push on upwards. The hill is one of those annoying ones that has lots of false summits. However, eventually I reach the top. There is a man sitting by a cairn. He is contentedly looking, admiring the view. I look at it too. The sense of calm that seems to emanate from him suffuses me and all my worries are lifted. I can see my future is bright."

'*Sniff pots*' – grass that has been freshly cut and crushed is a favourite. Smells are very evocative and this exercise is likely to bring out memories. The first time I used sniff pots was with two women in psychiatric intensive care. We all chose the cut grass pot to write about and the two patients both wrote about distant but happy memories of their families – one (who was unable to write so I scribed for her) related a childhood memory of Easter egg rolling in the park with her parents (who died many years ago) and siblings, and the other wrote about a happy memory with her brother who she has lost touch with because of her illness.

Writing about yourself, or someone else, doing some sort of hobby or other activity – either something you actually do (or used to do), or something you would like to do. In one session, at the suggestion of one of the patients, we did this exercise as a guessing game. We wrote obliquely, trying not to make it obvious what the activity was, and then read our pieces aloud while the rest of the group tried to guess the activity.

Collaborative poetry, e.g., writing a poem in a particular form such as this Kenning written in Spring 2011:

Spring

by Cate, Sally, Nigel, Jill and Carol

Day lengthener
Sun radiator
Snow melter
Earth warmer
Rain pourer
Puddle filler

Seed sprouter
Bud burster
Grass greener
Blossom bringer
Daffodil grower
Tulip kisser

Air cleaner
Life giver
Flesh warmer
Bunny breeder
Lamb springer
Bird singer

Life enhancer
Health promoter
Spirit raiser
Mood lifter
Music maker
Heart singer

Writing in a different 'person' or tense, e.g., writing about yourself in the third person, or writing about things that happened a long time ago, but in the present tense as if everything were happening right now. Writing about an experience in the third person can make you feel more detached and objective as you write.

Being adaptable

I believe it is vital to be flexible and adapt the planned programme, or even abandon it, depending on the group. I use open writing exercises so the writing produced can be developed according to individual preferences – whether that be some autobiographical writing, a poem, some descriptive or imaginative prose, or whatever. For example, Angela wrote a rhymed poem in every exercise where others in the group wrote unpolished prose. In another session Colin tried freewriting for the first time and later used what he had written as a starting point for song lyrics.

Sometimes a patient has something going on in their life that I can see would be a good thing for them to write about, e.g., I suggested to Betty that she write a letter from her future self, when she is well, to her small grandson to tell him how much he inspired her to get well. Betty's daughter has put the letter away in a box until the little boy is old enough to read it. To give another example: I had a one-to-one session with a woman who told me part way through the session that her mother had just died, and that she had been unable to get out of hospital to see her mother before she died. She mentioned that she had happy memories of her mother. So, I abandoned the second writing exercise I had planned and suggested instead that she write about one of her happy memories, which she did. She said afterwards how surprised she was that she hadn't cried when writing the memory about her mother and that she had found doing the writing comforting.

In any one session there could be one or two patients who have been to several of my groups and one or two newcomers. There can also be big variation in the writing skills and experience of the group members. So I try to choose writing exercises that are suitable for a relatively inexperienced newcomer, but different enough from previous weeks so the old hands don't get bored. The exercises need to be capable of being adapted at the last minute to suit the abilities and level of concentration of the group. They also

106

need to provide inspiration and challenge to the very experienced writers who occasionally attend.

I might decide to take some picture postcards to a session. The selection of cards I choose to take will depend on what stage of recovery the patients are likely to be in, e.g., photographs of beautiful landscapes are a good choice for psychiatric intensive care. But even with a given set of cards, I use them differently depending on the group. If I have a mixed group in terms of level of concentration and confidence for writing, I will probably ask everyone to choose a card that appeals and suggest that they could either write to describe what they see in the picture or choose to be more imaginative and write a bit of a story. Where everyone in the group is fairly confident about writing (for example when I have worked with them for several weeks) I would take a different approach. Here's an example: the group selects three cards and I decide on the order they will be used. For the first card we write for 2 minutes to describe what we see. For the second card we write what emotions the card inspires in us (again for 2 minutes). For the last card we each write the story we think the card is telling (for 10 minutes). Our stories, when we read them to the group, are always very different, which makes for an interesting and stimulating conversation. Other types of writing stimuli can be used flexibly too, e.g., objects, photographs of people, sniff pots.

Homework

Occasionally patients ask for homework, and even if they don't, I offer handouts giving ideas for creative writing, freewriting and journals/diaries. If I feel it is appropriate, I encourage people to write a little each day and especially to write a journal. Sometimes I feel it would be good for an individual to do a particular kind of writing within or outside the group and I discuss this possibility with them. While some people might benefit from writing out their feelings and thoughts, others might feel calmed from writing descriptively, e.g., about the natural world. Where someone is able to express their thoughts clearly and perhaps dwells on their worries too much, I might suggest they could get some distraction and intellectual stimulation by writing from the imagination.

Safety first

Although I do not deliberately direct participants to write about traumatic events, writing exercises can nevertheless bring up painful thoughts or memories. So, I don't rush off as soon as the session ends in case someone needs to talk or is upset and needs reassurance. I reassure where I feel able to, and contact a member of ward staff where appropriate.

When working in a mental health unit it is important to take appropriate precautions to safeguard yourself and the patients you work with. Before I start each session I collect an alarm, in case urgent assistance should be needed from qualified staff, and I talk to one of the nurses to find out whether there are any particular issues I need to be aware of while on the unit. I also regularly update my safety training. If I have any concerns about patients I raise them with ward staff immediately.

To continually improve my practice I write reflectively after almost every session and discuss anything I am unsure about in supervision meetings. Occasionally I use published methods or models of reflection in my journal (e.g., Johns, 1993; Bolton, 2010), but more often than not I just write down my thoughts in a fairly unstructured way, as in the following extract from my reflective journal.

Extract from reflective journal

Retrospective note: This session and several others at around the same time were longer than the scheduled hour because some of the participants were keen to have a longer session and include a coffee break, more writing, discussion of books, homework, etc.

Present: Carol, Nigel, Graham, Peter, Jill

Activity 1: What kind of weather are you? (used by permission of Gillie Bolton). This exercise went well. The patients all wrote positive things – sunshine on the hills, etc. I was the only one who wrote anything negative. Because I was feeling too hot I wrote that I was close, oppressive weather and that a thunderstorm was needed to clear the air.

*Activity 2: **Alpha write** (Adams, 2011) We thought of four words beginning with A as a collaborative exercise then we did some freewriting for each one. I explained that this is a good exercise to use in your personal journal, picking the next letter in the alphabet each day.*

*Activity 3: **Freewriting** We did 2 minutes freewriting for each of the colours black, blue, green and yellow.*

Reflections:

Graham came to the group for the first time today. He wrote relatively little owing to a lot of joint pain but he seemed to enjoy the writing and wrote thoughtfully and imaginatively. He was discharged the same day and so will not be coming to another session.

Jill has been coming to the group for several weeks now and seems at last to be participating a little more. But she still does not seem to me to enjoy the writing and doesn't write much so I think she may not be getting much benefit from it.

Peter is usually hesitant about writing in the group and is fairly quiet. This time he wrote more confidently and seemed actually to enjoy the writing. I think he surprised himself by writing more imaginatively than he expected.

Nigel always writes well and fluently but I am struggling to help him work out what he needs to write about. He can express his thoughts and feelings about his illness very clearly and I feel would probably benefit from writing about topics other than his illness to give his thoughts a different direction. I spoke to him after the session about 'flow' (Csikszentmihalyi, 2008) and suggested he might do some writing about his 'flow experiences'.

Graham and Peter engaged well with the session today, more so than I expected and I think more than they expected. I think they both enjoyed the writing exercises more than they expected too. However, I am not managing to really engage Jill with the sessions yet and need to give some thought to how I can do that: a one-to-one conversation with her might help if she would be willing.

I feel frustrated that I am not sure what kind of writing to recommend to Nigel. Sometimes writing seems to calm his anxiety somewhat, but some writing can make him more agitated. When he wrote once about his garden at home it set him off thinking that he would never be well again, living happily with his family and providing for them as he used to, which made him anxious and agitated.

Over the last few weeks the creative writing group has been the highlight of the week for Nigel, Cate, Sally and me. We have had some great discussions about writing, poetry and all sorts, and done lots of writing and sharing together. Cate and Sally were not at this session because they've been discharged, and I was conscious of missing them – which hasn't happened to me before in writing group.

Conclusion

In my inpatient writing groups I have met many lovely people at a time when they are in great mental distress. I encourage them to write because I strongly believe that writing can be therapeutic and so help people in their recovery. Research supports this view (see Chapter 1) as does the feedback I receive from patients (see Ross, 2011). Writing is a powerful tool and I hope this chapter has given you some ideas if you are thinking of leading wellbeing writing groups or using writing to help your own wellbeing or recovery from illness.

Acknowledgements

I would like to thank my practice supervisor and the staff of both the units in which I work for their support and encouragement, and the patients who write with me, share with me and even make me coffee on occasion. I would especially like to thank those patients who have kindly consented for some of their writing to be published here, and Cate for contributing a whole article (Part 2 of this chapter).

Note

Patient names have been changed throughout this chapter but I have been consistent with names, e.g., Cate, Sally and Nigel in Part 1 are the same people as in Part 2.

References

Adams, K. (2011). Alpha writes: 26 days to transformation. In: G. Bolton; V. Field; K. Thompson (Eds.), *Writing routes. A resource handbook of therapeutic writing* (pp. 72-74). London: Jessica Kingsley.

Bolton, G. (2010). *Reflective practice: Writing and professional development* (3rd edition). London: Jessica Kingsley.

Csikszentmihalyi, M. (2008). *Flow: The psychology of optimal experience.* Harper Perennial.

Flint, R.; Hamilton, F.; Williamson, C. (2004). *Core competencies for working with the literary arts for personal development, health and well-being.* London: Lapidus. Retrieved 28 February 2010 from http://www.lapidus.org.uk/ resources/fiona2.doc

Johns, C. (1993). Professional supervision. *Journal of Nursing Management, 1,* 9–18.

Normal, H. (1993) *Nude modelling for the afterlife.* Northumberland, UK: Bloodaxe Books.

Ross, C. A. (2011). Evaluation of Cumbria Partnership Year of Writing workshops. *Cumbria Partnership Journal of Research, Practice and Learning, 1,* 17-20. Retrieved 27 May 2011 http://www.cumbriapartnership.nhs.uk/uploads/Journal/CPJRPL%201%201%20Spring%202011%20p17%20Evaluation.pdf

Stiles, W. B., Gordon, L. E., & Lani, J. A. (2002). Session evaluation and the Session Evaluation Questionnaire. In G. S. Tryon (Ed.), *Counseling based on process research: Applying what we know* (pp. 325-343). Boston, MA: Allyn & Bacon. Edited version retrieved 22 January 2012 from http://www.users.muohio.edu/stileswb/session_ _questionnaire.htm

Tŷ Newydd. (2012). Tŷ Newydd: National Writers' Centre for Wales. Retrieved 26 January 2012 from http://www.tynewydd.org/

Recommended Reading

Adams, K. (1990). *Journal to the self: Twenty-two paths to personal growth*. Grand Central Publishing, New York.

Bolton, G. (2011). *Write yourself. Creative writing and personal development*. London: Jessica Kingsley.

Bolton, G.; Field, V.; Thompson, K. (Eds.). (2006). *Writing works: A resource handbook for therapeutic writing workshops and activities.* London: Jessica Kingsley.

Capacchione, L. (1989). *The creative journal: The art of finding yourself.* Van Nuys, CA: Newcastle Publishing.

King, L. (2002). Gain without pain? Expressive writing and self-regulation. In S. J. Lepore & J. M. Smyth (Eds.), *The writing cure: How expressive writing promotes health and well-being* (pp. 119–134). Washington DC: American Psychological Association.

Ross, C. A. (2012). *Words for Wellbeing*. Retrieved 22 January 2012 from http://www.cumbriapartnership .nhs.uk/words-for-wellbeing.htm

Part 2 – The Creative Writing Group

Cate Anderson

"aw, that sounds good," said my friend Sally. "We can both go together."
"What are you talking about?" I asked.
"Creative writing. It starts this Thursday," she replied.
"Never heard of it, and I doubt I have a creative bone in my body – especially at the moment!"

But Sally insisted we give it a try, and plus it would pass a couple of hours in the afternoon. Sally was good at writing. She had shown me a piece of work she had done previously and it was good: it held your attention right until the last minute.

So Thursday afternoon arrived and I dutifully went to the group with Sally. We met the lovely Carol Ross who would be taking the group. Initially I actually felt quite nervous: what if they were better than me or I didn't understand what was being asked of me? I would feel totally thick.

The group was quite small, with usually just three patients turning up most of the time, Sally, Nigel and I. Occasionally some other patients dipped in and out of the group. But three of us remained constant to the group with Carol.

After my initial reaction of being scared and worried about what the others would think it was amazing to see how my writing has changed over the weeks and how my mood and emotions affect the way I write. At the beginning Carol either gave us a picture or a word to write about – just whatever came into your head. It could just lead to other words or to a memory.

The first couple of weeks my mood was quite low and I had suicidal thoughts, and this was evident in my writing. For example: I chose to write about a picture of Striding Edge in the Lake District. First it started with a memory of completing that walk and the feeling of euphoria I had experienced on completing such a walk. I wrote about the fantastic view and the wonderful clear, fresh air. Then quite suddenly – just like my moods tended to do – the writing changed to quite dark thoughts about how now (because of my physical fitness, weight problem and lack of motivation) I wouldn't be able to attempt the walk, never mind complete it. Suicidal thoughts then began to creep in – if I could reach the top and jump off then I most definitely would die and I wouldn't be in this horrible mess.

As weeks passed and my condition started to improve my writing became more upbeat. It started to bring back memories, but these were happy memories – some that I hadn't thought of in years. The writing became more enjoyable and after the sessions my mood always seemed lifted and lighter.

For a couple of weeks we looked at poems and I remembered that I enjoy poetry. I had poetry books at home which hadn't been looked at in years, mainly because I always thought I didn't have time. It was great to go home and find those books and bring them in. Nigel and Carol had excellent voices for reading poetry and it was lovely to hear poems read out loud.

Carol started asking us to do a little bit of homework as such each week, and homework suddenly started to be fun. It didn't matter if I wasn't very good: nobody was bothered and we all tried to support and encourage each other every week. Sometimes one of us may be feeling quite low, so we would try and do an activity that might help lift their mood. We started having a coffee break and at those times we would chat about anything that took our fancy – it usually ended up with a laugh.

Then one week Carol asked us, using a prompt sheet, to create a character. My character turned out to be a ferret. Then Carol asked us if we might be able to write a short story about our character. The idea of writing a short story and making up a character really inspired me. I used the Knowledge Exchange room to research ferrets on the Internet – because I didn't know what baby ferrets are called, or where ferrets originated from. The biggest thing about this though was that I was quite excited about it. I was keen to go to the computer and further my knowledge and I really wanted to write a short story.

This was the first time in well over a year that I had had the motivation to do something and also to be interested in something other than thinking about work or family matters, or even harmful thoughts.

I am aware that lots of other things had been going on to help me achieve this, but creative writing really was the first thing I had got excited about in a long, long time. Thanks Carol!

A Guiding Light... by Gayle
(Written for my care coordinator)

Before we met I had lost my sight, fallen down from a colossal
    height...
Pain and hurt built up over years, clearly not wanting to be here,
    suppressed by my fears.
Living in a careless and chaotic world...
Eaten up by grief, distraught in floods of tears...
A tragedy waiting to happen, my mind eventually shattered.
Psychosis set in...My reality wasn't real.
Gripping onto my distant dreams with all my might...
You came along and shone a brilliant light!!
Ignited my hope and built up my strength and made me believe I
    could get through this and come out the other end
I was terribly defiant at first; you without doubt witnessed me at
    my worst...
But you were a constant, you never let go, with your help I turned
    a corner...I changed my world around.
I learned to love myself and keep my feet at all times on the
    ground!!
I found my passion for life!
A lot of love for the world!
My heart, stable mind, emotions and I gave birth to my precious
    baby girl
An enthusiastic Thai Boxer, looking after my outside to keep my
    inside well
A keen Artist, someday Art Therapist who knows!
I will be forever grateful... I think you're a star I want you to
    know!!!

Daffodil Walk by Debbie Mayes

The Ordnance Survey OL7 shows a blue line running through
    Staveley
but it doesn't show wild daffodils on an island in the river.
It shows a green tree symbol for woods
but it doesn't show a huge oak harbouring a polypody fern,
while roots as big as branches stretch across the damp earth.
The sign post says we have arrived at Cowan Head
but it makes no mention of the heady aroma of wild garlic
rising from beneath our feet.
The map shows the sewage works
but no hint of the pew, pew, pew, chwee, chwee of the nuthatch.
The signpost signals the Dales Way
but doesn't mention the lichen, fluorescent stains spat onto the
    rocks as by aliens.

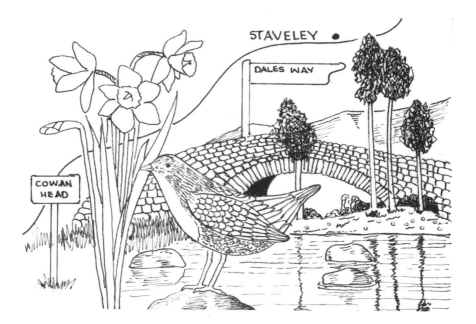

The map tells us of a chapel (remains of)
but not of moss covered logs laying like bodies in the cold ground.
A notice tells us we are in Beckmickle Ing Wood
but not of the grass growing on the wooden bridge over the river.
A weir is indicated on the map
but not the yellow star of Bethlehem growing nearby.
A sign warns 'danger deep water'
but this doesn't deter the dipper nesting beneath the bridge.

Strumpet by Sylvia Stevens

Flame red, she strides the sky,
goddess of the morning,
dancing in her gaudy dress
to impress: she fills the dawn
with frills, and flirts, daring
the wind to lift her skirt,
full-blown she flaunts
and flares in layers of lace,
and turns to burn the
rising mountain's face
in shameless scarlet,
careless of consequence:
for this is her moment
and she will have no
other colour, to blare
and blasé her
brazen beauty.

The Knowledge by Julie Callan

Rivers and mountains poetry keeps me sane.
The wisdom and connection with Nature,
take away the strain and the pain.

* I cannot be stopped.
* I cannot be stifled.
* I cannot be tied up in red tape
* nor bamboozled by gobbledegook.

Rivers and mountains go on forever.
It's a miracle, but I go on too,
in my way.

I am a rare crane
taking off.
The river shimmering silver below.
The mountains praising the skies.

I embrace the real world with my wings.
And I don't care if I'm dreaming.

Bang Flash by Lucy Hutton

I'm here, I think, it's an eerie silence
The land is barren and clear
All is dark the only light from a burning fence
I'm trying but nothing I hear
Is that something green, alive?
Time passes with sun and rain
Buds burst, flowers grow
Beauty in the world is back
All natural and green
The way it should have been
Who caused this?

Chapter 8 – At the Edge of a Deeper Calm
Marilyn Messenger

Beginnings

The catchy title of the elective module I chose in my first year as an undergraduate was, 'The mind meditation and contemporary creative practice'. As a mature student getting to grips with a BA (Hons) course in Creative Writing, meditation was yet another challenge for me.

When choosing an elective I was attracted by the idea that meditation might help my creative writing. In common with many writers, I have an 'inner policeman' who monitors my inventiveness, and I hoped that meditation might bypass this internal censorship. Also, the alternatives were practical in nature and I was daunted by the challenges of manipulating wet clay on a potter's wheel, or mastering the intricacies of digital photography. Embarking on a degree as a mature student had used up my reserves of adventurous spirit thus far, but I was intrigued by the idea of meditation and prepared to approach the module with interest and enthusiasm.

The instructions given in class were straightforward. We were to concentrate on the cool air gently inhaled through the nose and then focus on the soft warmth of exhaled breath. Our tranquil Buddhist tutor murmured in a calm, meditative tone that any superfluous thoughts should be eased from our minds.

However, being possessed of a 'busy' mind, I found it difficult to achieve any success in the classroom meditation sessions. No sooner had I cleared my mind of the trivia that filled it, than off it galloped on tangents of 'what ifs' and 'I wonder whys'. This was not helped by the fact that the human body is prone to treachery in situations where silence is required. I detected nearby stomachs rumbling like distant thunder. Noses whistled tunefully and the usually quiet act of swallowing became audible to me. Like orchestrated sound effects, they attracted my attention, though everyone else sat in quiet contemplation.

I did eventually manage a feeling of tranquillity when my thoughts quietened to a manageable distraction. At home however, I spent much time finding the most appropriate room/chair/position in which to meditate, rather like a dog treading circles in its basket before finally curling up, with a sigh. Once settled there were times when I approached the tantalising edge of a deeper calm and those small successes held promise.

The project

As part of the elective we were each given a project which began with a search for a special location in which to meditate. As a creative writing student, I was to follow that meditation with a writing session which would hopefully reflect the meditation in some way. I imagined a location near water, a lake perhaps, and I explored maps of the area around Keswick eventually being offered the use of a small cabin in woodland overlooking Derwentwater. In order to respect her privacy I will refer to the charitable lady owner of the cabin as E.

I have had numerous chance encounters with people who have been generous or kind to me and meeting E at her home was another of these. When mutual trust is established so swiftly, I am always filled with hope for all our futures. An unexpected conversation with a stranger who trusts you with their thoughts and concerns, their fears and dreams, is a joy.

What follows is taken from the journal that I wrote in the cabin at Derwentwater.

Home, 7.30am – Today I am going to spend some quality time with my mind and already I can sense it bounding ahead of me, as if it were a dog that senses a long and interesting walk. I have a feeling of excitement, of a treat in store. Now, as a result of my attempts at meditation, I almost regard my mind as a separate entity whilst still an integral part of me. I know how vital the mind is and that it has tremendous potential which is frequently overlooked. We all use our minds, but do we know how to make best use of them to achieve a happy and contented life? Do we treat our minds well?

Derwentwater – I was greeted by E and had coffee and a long chat at her kitchen table. People are treasure troves of fascinating memories and complex emotions. Finding the places where we touch, and share, with our minds is a very special experience that stays within and around you for the rest of your life. I discovered that E had a desire to write and I hope that I encouraged her to begin to write about events from her interesting past. We spoke about meditation and I found that she also found it difficult to compel her mind to be still.

We drove down to the cabin in an old Land Rover that jostled and bounced us along a rutted track through woods. Now I am alone in this idyllic setting. The cabin faces a miniature lake separated from Derwentwater by a narrow strand. The Keswick launch is moving across the gap in the trees and the sun glints on the lake. I can hear birds and a distant aeroplane, but little else until I become aware of the wind shivering the dry leaves on the beech trees and a pheasant giving one of those sharp, metallic cries that always startles. Perhaps the wind feels I have neglected its importance, because it grows stronger now, bumping the door against the cabin wall and stirring the curtains. A thin strand of cobweb sways across the window and captures the sunlight.

I am going to try and meditate now in the old wicker chair that faces the lake. I have been so inadequate at this so far that I don't expect anything wonderful. On the other hand, this is an amazingly beautiful place.

Derwentwater meditation

The meditation was my best yet and I was surprised to find that it had lasted for half an hour. It seemed to me that I closed my eyes for barely a minute. Such was my feeling of elation that I decided to capture the experience as the introduction to the creative writing that was to be the finale. As I explored the words in my head I knew that if my creativity lay in other directions I would be sweeping paint across canvas, or shaping clay to express my feelings at that moment.

It was more difficult than usual to calm my mind today given that it was full of the events of the morning. The distractions in the location were unfamiliar and interesting. Like a horse shying at a movement glimpsed from the corner of its eye, my mind was eager to prance and be unsettled. Slowly I achieved control and for a while enjoyed calm contemplation until this was followed by an almost audible 'snap' and I was aware of what I assume, in retrospect, was my mind. I was seeing, literally, with 'my mind's eye'.

There was an innermost focal area directly in front of me. This was neither light nor dark. It wasn't closed and pleated like a camera shutter, nor was it an opening. It wasn't symmetrical or solid, not flat, and not raised. It was just there, at the centre of my awareness. On either side surged fluid colour, rather viscous in consistency. The left side was green, as delicate and pale as the underside of a grasshopper. The right was a subtle feather grey. These areas of colour ebbed and flowed to the centre, but never over it, and where they met, above and below, they pooled into each other, touching but never mixing; a liquid jigsaw.

Watching these colours gently moving was incredibly restful and when I became aware of a thread of movement in the centre it didn't detract from the whole, but became a natural part of it. Tiny scarlet wires of 'electricity' sparked and flicked, until stilling to a symbol-like outline.

What followed

Words flowed into my mind and onto the page effortlessly.

And everything is sharper now, it really is. The spears of grass are emerald green; there is no other green to describe it. Fresh and bright against and around the soft charcoal remains of a bonfire. And life is full of endless possibilities, absolutely endless. A sailboat is slicing across the bay, a large leaf cutter beetle edges its way effortlessly across the window pane. Its body is shield shaped. Six legs move across the surface in no particular order. Should I put him outside? Or is he exactly where he wants to be? I don't know. I feel fizzy at so much detail out here. No two trees are the same in shape or colour and I can see them all. Why do we have so few words to describe trees and all of them inadequate? Nothing is still, how did I ever think it was? Every blade of grass, every leaf, ripples with life and above it all there are clouds which dare you to track their slow drifting.

I imagine a young woman walking through woodland looking for a place to be.

She had waited until the earth was soft and warm and smelled of life. The setting is perfect but then she had looked for such a place over the hot summer weeks. She plants her bare feet comfortably apart and curls her toes into the soil wriggles them as if in sand and, like sand, the soil gives way for her until only the curves of her ankles show. Slowly she raises her arms, stretches them above her head and fans out her fingers.

Foxgloves flourish around her calves as both limbs fuse and harden. Does she have regrets I wonder as the bark creeps around her waist and her arms divide into branches? I don't think so. She shakes her hair back and laughs aloud as the breeze lifts it and draws it up into the canopy. And then she is gone yet still there, in the pale silver of the bark in the slender tilt of a branch in the murmuring and rustle of her leaves in the steadfast beauty that catches and holds the eye.

Reflections

There was a difference in the writing following meditation that seemed to reflect a lack of self consciousness. Frequently when writing I am aware that I don't allow myself complete freedom. By this I mean that self imposed constraints develop along the lines of: what will people think of this, will they think I am writing about myself, or even worse, writing about them, despite the whole story being wholly fictional? Is my writing good enough; is that sentence or even that word right for the story? These limitations check creative flow but it is difficult to push away such self-imposed boundaries and 'let go of the sides' to discover what my capabilities are as a writer. I believe that meditation went a long way to achieving this.

Eleanor Rosch

I wanted to understand what brought about such a change after 30 minutes of meditation and so I searched for practitioners who have investigated the effects of meditation, feeling that if I could find someone whose work I could explore then I would learn more of the link between creative writing and meditation. This eventually brought me to papers written by Eleanor Rosch.

Eleanor Rosch is a Professor in the Department of Psychology at the University of California. Originally intending to study literature and take up writing as a career, she switched to philosophy in college and later to psychology. Rosch offers her views and then questions the logic behind them and it seems to me that she understands the questions that will be raised by her readers, or students, as a result of asking questions of her own life and practice.

An interview with C. Otto Scharmer (Rosch, 1999) was a measure of how highly Rosch was regarded by then, and how relevant meditation was to her own practice. At that time 'big business' was taking a look at possible alternatives to the then current methodology for inspiring management. The interview was part of an initiative 'Dialog on Leadership' and its ambitious aim was to find a new view of knowledge and leadership to inquire into "... the deeper foundations of leadership and change in an increasingly confusing and volatile world." (Scharmer, 2001).

Rosch was honest with Scharmer about her introduction to meditation and admitted that her first attempts weren't successful. She persevered and attended a 'Buddhist Practice Intensive Module' in Colorado and followed that with two weeks of meditation at a centre in the Rocky Mountains.

"I came back thinking, this is it this is really about something. I don't know what it's about but it's about something truly fundamental to people, and I'm going to pursue it and find out what it's about, and I know it's going to remake psychology." (Rosch, 1999).

In 2002 Rosch delivered a talk, 'What Buddhist meditation has to tell psychology about the mind' which clearly shows how meditation was strongly linked to her field of work – scientific psychology. Her opening sentence reflected how her thoughts on the subject had become clearer since the 1999 interview. "One of the best kept secrets of the last several centuries may be that some of what we classify as religious experience can make a fundamental contribution to scientific psychology." (Rosch, 2002).

Rosch spoke of how we shield ourselves against anything fundamentally new and so see meditative experiences as entering into an extraordinary state of mind rather than something normal and natural. I agree with this statement. The most open minded of friends will raise a quizzical eyebrow if you mention that you have become interested in meditation; include a reference to Buddhism and they may put a rescue plan together.

In psychology and cognitive science Rosch tells us that the mind is viewed as something separate to the body. This view is one that I think that many people either have, or have encountered. Mental illness is sometimes regarded in an entirely different manner to sickness of the body; as something to be ashamed of because of an implied loss of control.

The definition of psychology in the Shorter Oxford English Dictionary describes the science of the nature, functions and phenomena of the human soul or mind. The inclusion of those two descriptive words, 'soul or mind', illustrates how we are often portrayed as a composite form composed of body, mind and brain with the added complexity of soul. The brain may be viewed as the useful, intelligent, hard working component whereas the mind is where emotional turbulence lurks. The mind has the potential to be unstable or unpredictable. It's a place where you would find sentimentality and weakness. There is also the suggestion that we can be pushed out of this place by mental illness. For example, if someone becomes mentally unstable they are said to be 'out of their mind' or 'not in their right mind'.

Viewing the brain as a separate entity to the mind is supported by depictions in advertisements and health leaflets. The brain is tangible and is often portrayed as a living entity, perhaps suspended in fluid, as in sci-fi films. Most people would visualize the brain as pinkish grey, with a walnut-like surface, and know that, once removed, the brain is a tangible object and can be touched. But where is the mind situated, and what does it look like?

In my writer's imagination I see the mind as a swirling, ever changing and evolving vortex like a distant galaxy shot through with pinpoints of light and flashes of colour. As to where the mind is located, it is wherever and whenever we are. So, we divorce the two, brain and mind, and yet look at dictionary definitions of 'mind' and 'brain' and you will find them interchangeable.

Rosch refers to three Eastern traditions: Buddhism, Hinduism and Taoism, all of which have some reference to our "habitual state of mind" where we are totally bound to the material world and give little thought to "who we are, what is real, and how to act." This led to the main point of her talk in 2002, "There is an alternative way of knowing. And that alternative is seen as our original, natural, fundamental state, what we are right now, not any particular or special experience." (Rosch, 2002).

Rosch spoke of two modes of knowing: consciousness and awareness. She used a computer analogy to illustrate how the two work together. In other words we see a computer programme running, but that doesn't show us how it operates. Rosche referred to consciousness as awareness in disguise, they are not separate. The relevance of "... the specialism of Buddhism is to find awareness in the everyday experiences of consciousness itself, including all the senses, by means of cultivating intense mindfulness and intimacy with ongoing experience."

For me, flow, stream of consciousness, or free writing demonstrate this effectively.

"If you depict a bird give it space to fly"

In her paper, "If you depict a bird give it space to fly': On mind meditation and art' Rosch aimed to show that "...meditation and art can illuminate each other and can do so beyond particular artistic styles or practices". (Rosch, 2005). She acknowledged that scientists are generally considered to be the experts when it comes to understanding the human mind. Yet we somehow intuitively know that there is more to it than their image of a mind isolated from the world, constantly striving to develop new skills, with a prevailing purpose of survival and reproduction.

Rosch believes that the creative arts tap into this fundamental intuition and suggests that they do this by their ability "...to show people in a mirror which reflects their ordinary self image in the light of these broader and deeper intuitions." (Rosch, 2005). Whilst accepting that the world of the arts is vast and that much analysis has taken place concerning the many different cultures and practices within it, Rosch offered a basic premise. Through the arts we can know ourselves on a much deeper level than in everyday life. Furthermore, meditation can help this process as it "... serves not only to calm and focus the mind, but to begin to integrate the person: to bring body, mind and action together, to bring the senses and their objects (the seen, heard thought...) together". (Rosch, 2005).

Rosch speaks of being moved, sometimes in a lasting way, by visual images or narratives - including fictional. The main reason for the arts having such an impact Rosch attributes to being able to experience creative art without the ego getting in the way. "Perception (and the resulting habits and consciousness), from the point of view of the ego mind, always filter experience through personal hopes and fears. ...there is an underlying mode of immediate perception without the bias of hope and fear concerning one's self. Note that this is not a state of indifference ..." . (Rosch, 2005).

Rosch ended the 2002 paper with specific advice to psychologists and cognitive scientists to take meditation and the arts very seriously. "Are not psychology and cognitive science supposed to be about real people and real minds?" (Rosch, 2005). Clearly meditation had become an integral part of her life and her work.

Eleanor Rosch's work is both absorbing and inspiring. Initially I was concerned that her writing would be weighty or overly intellectual, given her stature in the field of psychology, but this was not the case. Her ideas and the reasoning behind them make good sense and if her views on the importance of meditation and the arts were more widespread then I really feel there could be a shift, not only in the way we approach creativity, but also how we view each other.

Waves on the ocean

I related to Rosch's early experience of meditation as being worthwhile but requiring tenacity. It was puzzling to me that I should have to struggle to quieten my mind or clear it of trivia. Sometimes it felt like a battle of wills, as if part of me was resisting and I wondered why it was so difficult. Rosch offered the following:

> "One thing about meditation; the word doesn't refer to any specific thing. There are innumerable markedly different practices each aiming at a different result that we lump together as 'meditation.' The particular techniques are never, in their home traditions, the point. Having a blank mind is not the point per se of any Buddhist sitting practice I know of. Occasionally we may have an experience of mental blankness but that is another experience, another 'wave on the ocean', like having thoughts or emotions of various kinds, sleepiness etc. So don't be discouraged if you have a 'wild mind' it's a mind." (Rosch, 2008).

Now, if meditation does not result in an inspired writing session then I know that is fine. I understand that I am not doing anything wrong and I no longer regard meditation as a challenge or test that I might fail. What I do feel, as a result of meditation, is the freedom to freefall when writing; to let the words gather speed across the paper without restraint or limitation.

Reflecting on the effects on the writing which followed the meditation at Derwentwater I see elements that were new, for me and to me. The observations and feelings I experienced were something 'other' and something to give more thought to.

And so the project's end became a beginning for me. I was about to write 'life is full of surprises' but 'life' isn't the word I need. Everything that I learnt was about that elusive something else, something essential in everyone, a kind of human magic that we can all access. It has the potential to hover at the edge of our lives or to rush in to heal and astonish. This chapter is one step forward for me as it includes feelings and thoughts written without my personal censorship and now set down for others to read. A door has opened and, though not yet flung wide, my metaphorical foot is wedged in the gap. I will let Eleanor Rosch bring this chapter to a close.

> "Art at its best presents a recipe for awake daily life. May we all be able to tap into that." (Rosch, 2005).

References

Rosch, E. (1999). *Primary knowing: When perception happens from the whole field.* Interview conducted by Claus Otto Scharmer, October 15. Retrieved 21 October 2011 from http://www.presencing.com/presencing/dol/Rosch-1999.shtml

Rosch, E. (2002). *What Buddhist meditation has to tell psychology about the mind.* Talk delivered at The American Psychological Association, August 23. Retrieved 21 October 2011 from http://anti-matters.org/articles/3/public/3-3-1-PB.pdf

Rosch, E. (2005) "If you depict a bird, give it space to fly": On mind, meditation, and art. In J. Baas & M. J. Jacobs (Eds.), *Buddha Mind in Contemporary Art*. Berkeley, CA: University of California Press. Reprinted in M. McLeod. (2005). *Best Buddhist Writings* 2005. Boston: Shambhala Publications. Retrieved 21 October 2011 from http://psychology.berkeley.edu/faculty/profiles/erosch2005.pdf

Rosch E, (2008). Personal correspondence.

Scharmer, C. O. (2001). *Dialog on Leadership*. Sponsored by McKinsey & Company and the Society for Organizational Learning (SOL). Retrieved 21 October 2011 from http://www.presencing.com /presencing/dol/about.shtml

'Cross the Sands of Morecambe Bay by Andy Mortimer
(with some help from Rudyard Kipling)

By the old clock tower in Arnside, lookin' westward to the sea
Cedric, the Guide, is waitin' for the likes of you and me;
He walks the sands for charities and with sponsorship you pay,
From Whitecreek Bay to Kents Bank, 'cross the sands of Morecambe
  Bay.
'Cross the sands of Morecambe Bay,
Where the winds and quicksand play,
Where the tides come in like horses on the flat at Derby Day.
'Cross the sands of Morecambe Bay,
Join the walkers while you may.
Come rain or shine it's good for health, whatever some might say!

And when the rain is lashin' and river Kent is runnin' high,
Across will go the walkers with the water up to thigh.
Whatever their age or state of health, they all enjoy the fun –
Hundreds cross whenever it's safe – most walk but some
  might run.
'Cross the sands of Morecambe Bay,
Where the winds and quicksand play,
Where the tides come in like horses on the flat at Derby Day.
'Cross the sands of Morecambe Bay,
Join the walkers while you may.
Come rain or shine it's good for health, whatever some might say!

And, if you're feelin' knackered when you finally reach your goal,
At least you're not in quicksand nor have fallen down a hole.
So for this you must thank Cedric and his knowledge of the Bay,
Remember him and don't begrudge the blisters on the way.
'Cross the sands of Morecambe Bay,
Where the winds and quicksand play,
Where the tides come in like horses on the flat at Derby Day.
'Cross the sands of Morecambe Bay,
Join the walkers while you may.
Come rain or shine it's good for health, whatever some might say!

An Afternoon in the Garden by Hilary Tattershall

The cloudless sky is reflected in the river's gentle flow, and its particular blue is the perfect backdrop to green trees and grasses along the banks outside the garden. From the terrace I can see the brewery's old maltings and the silhouette of the broken castle, as the river curls away to the east.

Inside the garden's old walls the sunlight bathes every living thing in vivid technicolour. I can feel the warm caress of the afternoon sun on my hair, and a slight breeze plays with my fringe and along my bare arms. Standing on the broken slate path, the scent of flowers from all parts of the garden wafts towards me on the breeze, the perfume coming and going. The great bed of old roses, arching over the path and bearing the faces of its many flowers to the sun, is the source of much of the scent. Tall blue and white flowered borage and pink poppies are alive with bees and their buzzing.

My task is weeding – how dull that sounds, and hard work on a warm afternoon. It is in fact heaven to work in a garden on a day like today.

The young herb plants in line at the end of the beds have found their new home congenial, and after only a month have grown wider and taller in the black topsoil. They have been accompanied by a crop of weeds, still small but smugly settling their roots in the fertile conditions. On my hands and knees, protected by a rubber kneeler, I prod around the weeds carefully with a hand fork, and the soil falls aside easily to allow the weeds to be extracted. Before tossing the little weed plants into a tub, I brush off the fine topsoil so it is not wasted. Then I fork over the tilth to even it, and obliterate the place where the weed was recently growing.

I notice small clumps of grass beyond reach in the middle of the wide bed. Standing up I stretch out a hoe, and can just get its edge under the clump to lever it out. The roots give up with little struggle, and I can lift the clump with the hoe to drop it into the tub. Using the hoe, I gently chop up the soil whence came the grass, and notice how much blacker the soil becomes as it is hoed.

The tool is light and well-balanced, perfect for the job, and allows delicate movements to get between the plants without damage. The soil hardly resists, and trickles like water over its blade.

I stand back to review my progress, and notice other weeds requiring attention. The repeated movements of the hoe - gently pushing, levering and lifting, followed by light chopping, are soothing and undemanding – just right for a warm afternoon.

The sun on the top of my head is hotter now, and my neck is damp from the effort of innocent work. I feel pleasure at the improvements I've made in the condition and the appearance of the bed, and I just want to go on and on.

Workday Blues (Penelope Elias)

Commuter town
Is where I live;
It gets me down
But I'll survive.

It's no use
Harping on regrets:
I can choose
What to forget.

My pleasure
May be small
But I treasure
Them all.

And who yet knows
What lies ahead?
Adversity's blows
Disguise the sound of hope's firm tread.

Red Rucksack by Carol Ross

It's lasted well,
his red rucksack.
Zip often strained to bursting
but not bursting.

Thin and light when empty
bulky and heavy as he
jogs and it bobs
down our road and
across the field
to school.

And such a comfort
the brilliant red of it.
I see it as a small
scarlet blur
crossing the school yard
safely arrived
unaware of my gaze.

It has lasted well
but its days are
numbered now.
Big school beckons.
The new cool black bag
already waiting in the hall,
making the old look
childish and small.

Chapter 9 – Saved by Stories: A Case Study
Vee Howard-Jones

Preface

This is a story about a man saved by stories.

The man – Patrick – was my client in an Occupational Health Counselling Service. I was his Counsellor and we were both trying to keep him alive.

What follows is our story of how reading the creative writing of others helped to keep him in the world.

At the time, Patrick was a married man in his sixties with two grown up daughters. He had worked at his current employment as an engineer in a huge factory setting for more years than he cared to mention. He'd worked all his life right from joining the Navy when he was 16, and indeed, when I first met Patrick he reminded me of an avuncular Captain Birdseye, all twinkly blue eyes and snow-white beard.

He didn't look depressed – if depression has a look about it. I've come to discover through my years of working with clients and in my own experience, that Depression can wear a mask. Churchill had his 'Black Dog'. Clients have variously described their own Depression to me as a black hole; a black room with the windows painted and the light turned off; feeling cut off from the human race; being dead inside – a zombie. A fog. An absence of light – no light at the end of the tunnel; buried alive, suffocating. Many times it can seem like an unwelcome intruder – an alien. It can take residence, squat, viscous and cloying and suck the life-force from its host.

And there I go too – making Depression the Enemy – something with its own personality. Very often Depression is personified by its sufferers, the self-help army and by the media. The big D. It can become the Foe – to beat, struggle with, to combat, fight, disarm, and manage. To accept that our darkest thoughts, feelings and behaviours are part of ourselves – seems unacceptable somehow.

The light in Patrick's eyes belied his Depression. I knew he was depressed – his Beck's Depression (Beck, Rush, Shaw & Emery, 1979) and Anxiety (Beck & Steer, 1993) Inventories told me so. What the forms don't tell you though is how the complex intricacies of disappointments, losses, fears and wariness become established from childhood to adulthood. How learning to not trust anyone, including the self, can become a familiar, if not a particularly helpful, coping strategy.

Patrick had been referred to the Occupational Health Counselling Service because of his difficulty with relationships with other workers – especially managers. It seemed that Patrick had the capacity to be involved in conflict quite easily and was seen as moody, argumentative and difficult. Despite this, he was a valued, experienced and efficient employee, albeit one who did not suffer what he thought of as fools gladly. An argument with a male colleague had resulted in Patrick facing disciplinary procedures and taking sick leave. It was suggested that counselling might be useful for him, and he eventually agreed, having never sat in a room with anyone – never mind a woman – and talked about his innermost thought-machinery.

There are as many ways of therapy as there are religions. In fact, engaging in the therapeutic process can seem like an act of faith – a leap into the unknown. The Therapeutic Church in the UK today is Cognitive Behaviour Therapy (CBT). CBT works on the premise that our thoughts, feelings, physiology and behaviour interrelate and that people can become involved in ways of thinking that are not useful to them. A change in our thinking, the CBT literature states, can result in us having different feelings which will impact on our bodily responses and thus result in a change in behaviour. CBT, through extensive research, has been proven to be effective.

I was originally trained in a person-centred approach whose core concepts are that it is through the engagement in a therapeutic relationship that healing and growth occur. This relationship needs to contain the core elements (or conditions) of empathy, genuineness and respect from the therapist which is conveyed to the client.

Over years of working with trauma (and having experienced it myself) I had become interested in the work of Irvin Yalom, an Existential Psychotherapist. Existential Psychotherapy is a therapy that stems from philosophy. Therapists working in this way believe that our depression and anxiety can stem from our struggle with the acceptance of our non-being, our ultimate loneliness, the chaos that comes with the thoughts that there are ultimately no rules and that life has no meaning – except that which we give it.

I work as an eclectic therapist, which to my mind is a therapist who believes that one size does not fit all – and that sometimes a bespoke tailored therapy, as individual to the client as the client is to the world – is essential in discovering what it is that ails us.

In our first two sessions I felt Patrick testing me out – was I trustworthy or was I part of The Establishment? Patrick did not mention at first his decision to end his life. He talked more about his difficulties at work and how he couldn't leave because he felt pressure from his family to earn the optimum pension. It emerged that Patrick had a history of abuse from those who considered themselves in authority over him – from the Irish orphanage at the age of three years right through to the present day. What Patrick learned was those who had dominion over him were not necessarily smarter, kinder or more responsible than him.

Patrick is an intelligent, logical, rational thinker. He is interested in world events, politics, philosophy, religion and with a quirky and wicked sense of humour. However, Patrick lived in a world where he was constantly translating, and many times misinterpreting, people's facial expressions, gestures, intonation, words – he felt like a stranger in a strange land.

It felt very important that Patrick and I had an open, collaborative, non-judgemental relationship; one where I ceaselessly tried to see the world through his sparkling, inquisitive eyes.

Patrick had started to talk openly and fearlessly about his non-being. He thought constantly about suicide because he believed his family would be financially better off if he was dead, than if he stayed alive and eventually retired. It seemed that he had very little regard for his existence and each day was another pointless trudge through the mire of petty power plays, trivialities and the engagement of all the stuff that doesn't really matter. This was his biggest secret. No one could tell that Patrick was burdened by his existence. He was a consummate actor. He did not for one minute believe that his wife and daughters would miss him if he chose to end his life. Rather that they would be better off by getting his full pension benefits. Depression can skew our version of reality. When a person feels worthless they start to believe they are worthless and look for evidence to back that belief up.

So for Patrick, death seemed like a logical and rational conclusion to the problem of his painful feelings about being alive. He did not believe in an afterlife or that beyond the grave there was redemption.

Patrick hadn't so much as lost God as kicked Him out and slammed the door in His face. He was a lapsed Catholic whose childhood had been spent in an Irish children's home. He had seen and experienced cruelty delivered in the name of God and had no further truck with the concept. We talked together about finding a way to live with the absence of a deity and what it means to have the belief that there is no one watching – either in a protective or pejorative sense.

I knew that Patrick was an avid reader of current affairs and nonfiction. He'd continued to read throughout feeling depressed which is unusual. Very often people find that they do not have the attention span for sustained focussed thought that reading a book requires. However, reading was one way of escaping from his family's scrutiny and concerned looks.

I experienced him as a very visual person despite his protestations to the contrary. Patrick believed he had no visual memory. He said he referred to me as 'The Lady', being unable to remember my name or my face. However, in counter-balance to this, his stories about his life were rich with images and colour. Ironically, it was negative images that Patrick recalled most vividly and which therefore taunted and threatened him.

Introducing Patrick to books that mirrored in metaphor some of what he had been conveying to me, seemed like the next logical step. I was interested in Bibliotherapy from when I first heard the term – realising that I had been using it all my life. The solace in disappearing into another's world and through metaphor achieving enlightenment or new understanding about one's life is not new.

The first book: *Man's Search for Meaning* by Viktor Frankl. The existential precipice – or deciding to live or not

I asked Patrick if he would be interested in reading some things that were encapsulating the feelings and ideas of what I thought I heard him saying. Patrick agreed and this is where I introduced him to Vicktor Frankls' *Man's Search for Meaning* (Frankl, 1946).

Man's Search for Meaning is a true account of Frankl's incarceration in four Nazi concentration camps. It is a harrowing tale of striving for existence in the most deprived and traumatically cruel of conditions. During his incarceration Frankl, a psychotherapist, neurologist and psychologist, became an observer in the ways and means of survival. He noticed that those who could find meaning in tasks they were involved in (whether digging in a frozen ditch, or comforting others), or who could retain a vision of and hope for the future, seemed to have more chance of enduring the hardships of the camp. Frankl remembered the words of Nietzsche who is quoted as saying: "He who has a why to live for can bear with almost any how" (cited in Frankl, 1946, p.84). Frankl's meaning in the concentration camp became the exploration of how others derived meaning from suffering. Frankl's father, mother, brother and wife all died whilst he was in captivity.

139

Frankl's words resonated with Patrick: "everything can be taken from man but one thing: the last of the human freedoms – to choose one's attitude in any given set of circumstances, to choose one's own way no matter the circumstance" (Frankl, 1946, p.75). Patrick felt trapped in his work. He dreaded walking into the building and would experience high levels of anxiety. He told me that the only meaning he had to keep him alive at that time was our talks together. I felt dismayed and sad too. I could see the obvious qualities that Patrick had – compassionate, a striver for rights and equality; funny, smart, a good father and husband, loyal, passionate about the world – yet he didn't feel or see these things at the moment. Could I help him find meaning in our encounters, long enough to help him dislodge his depression?

The second book: *The Book Thief* by Markus Zusak

Patrick had talked about how he had identified with Frankl's description of the Holocaust and that he had always been interested in this aspect of history as the discrimination resonated with his experience of being an Irish man in Britain in the early 1960s. He talked about the discrimination he felt, and the empathy he had with his Afro-Caribbean colleagues. Patrick felt he was only discriminated against when he opened his mouth to speak, and therefore felt more fortunate than black immigration workers who were immediately identified as different because of their colour. This meant that Patrick learnt to keep his mouth shut for himself, but found his voice in the defence of others.

Patrick still talked in a matter of fact manner about his decision to kill himself. He had promised me that he would not do this whilst in therapy – so it felt like there was a lot riding on the work we did together. I felt it was important to trust Patrick and to engage him in a serious discussion about death and his consideration to leave life. Continuing the theme of the Holocaust, I sent him *The Book Thief* (Zusak, 2007).

The Book Thief is a beautifully written and heart-rending account of the life of a young orphan, Liesel, who lives with her foster family during the Nazification of Germany. Liesel 'acquires' a number of books – the words of which have significant relevance to her life and the community around her. Death is the narrator of *The Book Thief*. Death has taken an interest in Liesel and follows her life with curiosity from the death of her brother and the stealing of her first book. The book is a testimony to the triumph of human spirit and kindness over the experience of adversity and the power of words to excite and move us. The discovery of that power is the backdrop to the creation of some of the most finely drawn characters that I have ever read. No one can read about Hans Luberman, Liesel's foster father, without believing that he has existed as part of our lives, so beloved and familiar does he become. Despite this description, which nowhere near does it justice, *The Book Thief* is a life affirming book; tender, spiritual and to my mind essential reading for all.

Patrick and I talked about the meaning he gained from the book. He opened up more about his own childhood which had been beset with unfairness and others making decisions about his life that had significant negative impact on him. Patrick said that there would be fewer problems in life if "people had more hugs from their Mammies." He reflected on the distant relationship with his own mother and the fact that she came in and out of his life, leading to him spending a large amount of time in a children's home with his sisters, not receiving the hugs he craved and ultimately learned to live without. How must it feel to be in an orphanage, while one of your parents still lived?

The third book: On justification and perception – *The Kindly Ones* by Jonathon Littell

Patrick was talking less about ending his life and was moving towards conjecture about what he would do with his life if he took the leap and left the company on early retirement. However, rather than moving towards a new phase, it appeared he was still moving away from what he perceived as an intolerable and unfair position. We talked about how, when he felt aggrieved, he would take his emotional ball home and withdraw himself, hurt and angry, from others. This strategy seemed to cause him more pain than it did those from whom he had withdrawn. There are a wealth of books which reflect on the complexities of human relationships, but there was one which I thought would resonate most for Patrick. I sent him *The Kindly Ones* (Littell, 2009).

The Kindly Ones is narrated by Maximillian Aue who is a high ranking SS officer whose mission is to oversee the massacre of 50,000 Jews in the Ukraine, amongst many other heinous acts. What makes this book significant is the calm, clear rhetoric of the intelligent and cultured protagonist who is wholly committed to the goals of the Third Reich and its Final Solution. Max Aue is a monster who would not think of himself as such. This might sound like a very strange book for therapy given its traumatic subject matter and the author's painstaking attention to every detail. However, Patrick declared it as "the best of all treatments you have given me." Patrick prided himself on his logical and pragmatic approach to problems – he could never understand why others seemingly did not operate in this way – managers at work for instance, and colleagues. This cognitive dissonance between the way that people seemingly behaved against reason and logic meant that Patrick experienced high stress levels and would feel persecuted by others as he had no way of explaining their behaviour towards him. What followed then for Patrick were disillusionment, despair and subsequent depression. It would seem that this book gave Patrick an understanding of how cognitively others justify their actions. *The Kindly Ones* helped Patrick find a new perspective where he felt able to detach himself more from the perceived reactions of others. It helped him to realise that he was seen as part of a workforce and that certain rules, attitudes and behaviours in the workplace were not particularly targeted at him personally.

The last book: *The Ragged-trousered Philanthropists* by Robert Tressell

Our final book *The Ragged-trousered Philanthropists* (Tressell, 1914) has been credited as the book that helped the Labour party have a landslide victory in the election just after the Second World War. It follows the lives of a group of working class men and their families trying to eke a living whilst the rich get richer and the poor get closer to the workhouse, the almshouse or the grave. It is a tale of exploitation of hard working, moral people by 'fat cat' capitalists. It is essentially a Socialist Party manifesto. Patrick identified with the working men, written about with such tender good humour and pathos. Tressell's book helped him reinforce his decision to leave work and also helped him to focus on the positives of such a move. Patrick started to talk about the peace he would find, the hobbies he would pursue. He planned holidays and a trip to visit a daughter on the other side of the world. He was no longer running away, but running towards.

We ended our work together as Patrick left the organisation.

Stories are important. It is through stories that we are able to find a narrative that fits with our own lives. Stories give us hope, make us cry, thrill, laugh, delight, cope with our fear and loneliness. But more importantly they give us the opportunity to see through the eyes of others.

References

Beck, A. T.; Rush, A. J.; Shaw, B. F.; Emery, G. (1979). *Cognitive therapy of depression*. New York: Guildford Press.

Beck, A. T.; Steer, R. A. (1993). *Beck anxiety inventory manual*. San Antonio, TX: The Psychological Corporation Harcourt Brace & Company.

Frankl, V. E. (1946). *Man's search for meaning*. USA: Beacon Press.

Littell, J. (2009). *The kindly ones*. USA: Harper Collins.

Tressel, R. (1914). *The ragged-trousered philanthropists*. Ireland: Grant Richards.

Zusak, M. (2007). *The book thief*. USA: Knopf.

Moments with Cancer by Andy Wild

Bruised, battered and a bit bewildered,
Trying to make sense of it all.
Trying to keep it together
And not make me feel so small.

It's the medication and the fatigue
And the medicals and the "what I was"
It's the money and the battle
And having to say "because......."

We all die you know and that's ok;
It's good to know before you go.
Maybe a bit less tired would have been better.
But Hayley's here now – always now –
Two years old and ferocious with life –
What a star!
Burning bright with worlds ablaze
A life of love and bless'ed rage.

Hayley – First Thing
In the morning I lie in bed awake.
Sometimes for a while.
I want to get up,
I want to have my coffee.
But even more –
I want to hear your feet thumping across the floor,
Waiting for you to give me that big,
Morning, face to face hug.
I can wait the world for that.

Wrote for My Molly When She Was Seven
by Donna-Louise Curwen

Today she started in year three... dressed in St Begh's burgundy
Looking older and ohhh so grand, but young enough to still hold
    my hand.
My heart was hurting I found it hard, to walk her into that school
    yard...
I tried to smile it was the right thing to do. She rolled her eyes
    and said this is not year two...
I am a big girl now and I will be fine, I felt her little hand squeeze
    mine.
I love you Mam, its ok to go. I whispered Molly, I love you more...
I walked away and turned to see, my little girl smiling big at me...
The dreaded first morning is over once more, then next time we
    take on year four!!!!!!

How May I Help You? by Ian Richmond

I can remember
How the factories roared
And the night sky turned red
When the hot steel was poured.

Now how may I help you?
I hear every day
In a measured inflexion
That implies that they care.

I can remember
When the steel works shut down
And a sense of despair
Fell over the town

How may I help you?
You can give me my pride
You can bring back the shipyards
To the banks of the Clyde

I can remember
When they came to tell
Of corporate headquarters
And call centre hell

How may I help you?
You can give back my soul
And a life that is more than
An escape from the dole.

Chapter 10 – Story-Sharing in Healthcare – Creative Communication for Wellbeing

Elizabeth Gates

No-one needs professional training to tell stories. We use them on a daily basis to build friendships, resolve conflicts, explain who we are and illustrate who we'd like to be. Every time we are late, we tell a story. The later we are, the better the story. We can all tell stories.

But story-sharing in a healthcare setting – with healthcare's powerful relationship to the keenest human concerns – is a potent tool. And its uses are many.

To illustrate, here is the story of Managua children's hospital director Fernando Silva doing his rounds before going home for his own Christmas.

> " . . . [Silva] heard cottony footsteps behind him. He turned to find one of the sick children walking after him. In the half light he recognized the lonely doomed child. Fernando recognized the face already lined with death and those eyes asking for forgiveness, or perhaps permission. Fernando walked over to him and the boy gave him his hand. 'Tell someone,' the child whispered. 'Tell someone I'm here.'"

Entitled 'Christmas Eve' and originally written down by Eduardo Galeano, this story has been re-told many times by world-renowned story-teller University of Chicago Professor Arthur Frank (Frank, 2010).

Frank is captivated by it. For him – and for me, as a story-teller in my own right – it is immensely powerful. And, in the traditions of memoir, biography and journaling, it demonstrates one fundamental use for story-sharing: bearing witness to existence.

What is more, although in practical terms I am impotent to help, I am now connected to that dying child – and all others like him. And, because you have now heard his story, you are too. World-wide, into the past and into the future, stories constantly connect us to each other.

But story-sharing in healthcare can offer yet more benefit. Story has the capacity to convert testimony and connection into positive action and this is perhaps story-sharing's most wonderful gift to healthcare.

Moya Sayer-Jones, founder of 'Only Human Communication' understands this well. In 2006, she was story-gatherer for 'In My Life' – an Australian-based project examining the concerns of illicit drug users' families. Drug users, the project concluded, fare better when they live with their families. But the book, *In My Life* (Sayer-Jones, 2006) – which grew out of the project – allows these families to share their story. In their own words, with no punches pulled, their stories enabled their 'voices' to be heard (see Only Human Communication, 2006).

But the value of story-sharing does not end with a testimony to the feelings of those involved. As Moya Sayer-Jones explains:

> "During the writing of In My Life, I met a woman who told the story of her failure to help her daughter Maddie through her battles with drug addiction. She had eventually lost her to an overdose eight years before. This mother's own health, both emotional and physical, had been ravaged by the trauma and strain of her daughter's addiction: the many suicide attempts, mental health battles, brushes with the law and death. The mum was fifty-two years old but looked much older and carried enormous guilt that she had not done enough to help. Despite counselling, she had not been able to free herself of the regret. On this day, I had brought a draft of the story based on our conversations. As she finished reading, she put down the manuscript and tears trickling down her face, she said, 'I see now that I did try. I did do my best. There was nothing more that I could do.'"

The impact of a 'good' story is always profound. And, at that pivotal moment for story-teller and story-gatherer, says Moya: "I decided to leave my work as a fiction writer and concentrate solely on using Story for better health outcomes."

And, she continues: "It's now six years since that conversation and the mother has picked up the lost strains of her life and health. She is working in her career again (nursing) and is enjoying her life with her son and grandchildren."

As noted by Alida Gersie, who developed the model of Therapeutic Story-Making (Gersie, 1997), through telling their own story, patients can:

- Communicate information about their own condition;

- Develop insights into their own situation by being obliged to offer truthful explanations of their own thoughts and feelings and actions;

- Be empowered by taking ownership of their own experiences.

But the success of a patient's story-sharing depends on the listening skills of the audience and, as experts note, ideal levels of listener quality among healthcare workers can be elusive. By nature of the healthcare context, listening skills are severely tested – as is the capacity to interpret what is heard. And reasons for this abound.

For example, as Dr Rita Charon explains (2008, p.99), the stories of the sick "come out chaotically, achronologically and interwoven with bits of life and the past."

She continues, optimal staff-patient communication occurs when a health professional, listening attentively, can "competently and naturally absorb, recognize, interpret and comprehend the value of all that patients tell."

There is a simple strategy to achieve this. As she suggests: "Through training in reading, in writing, in reflecting, in decoding these many gestures of life-writing, health professionals can readily become dutiful and powerful readers of their patients' illness narrative."

Charon (2006) records some vivid stories of faltering or failing doctor-patient interaction. She analyses where this breaks down – usually when the patient tells one story of their life and the health professional hears another.

In my view, this mishearing is multi-factoral. It may arise from pressure of work, fear of litigation, ignorance, lack of confidence, arrogance and stress – to name a few. But, the healthcare professional's listening skills may also be impeded by the 'background noise' of their own story – in transactional analysis terms, their own lifescript.

For the healthcare professional, their own 'story' may have assumed mythic overtones almost impossible for merely mortal creatures to match. In the myths, legends and folklore we have all internalised since Story began, the Shaman (or in modern terms, the 'health professional') must lead people through difficult transformations – such as from health to sickness, from sickness to death or from sickness to health. This is a tall order for a health professional straight out of college – even though fulsomely equipped with clinical knowledge and well-versed in ethical practice.

As Dr Charon identifies, what good healthcare requires of its personnel is heightened self-awareness and a capacity for sincere empathy. And Story can play a strong role here.

For several years now, medical educators have argued for the inclusion in medical education of medical humanities – in particular the study of literature (which is, after all, 'Story'). And, with the value of the work of creative writing and story practitioners and bibliotherapists now recognized, Charon's ideal of empathic interpretation of patient narrative can more easily be realised.

But there may be further difficulties. A sickness story may be delivered with high levels of skill. Its language may record vivid sensory detail. There may be variation in pace and tone which intrigues. And the patient may skillfully repeat words and phrases to emphasise and communicate meaning. But the story must also deliver what the audience needs to know. And this demands a high degree of linguistic ability in people whom Arthur Frank has designated 'wounded story-tellers' (Frank, 1995).

But this can be done. One new patient was reported as having told and re-told the story of his illness eight times in eight different ways to eight different healthcare workers, all of whom had a different interest in his case.

And, through their stories, Professor Frank says, the ill can contribute to the creation of these desirable empathic bonds between themselves and their healthcare professional listeners.

In fact, he emphasises, the seriously ill need to become story-tellers – even if wounded – to recover the "voice that illness and its treatment often take away."

And, as those 'wounded storytellers' share their experiences, their voices take on their own authority. They create a pool of wisdom about how to survive major illness and trauma with dignity. And when this achieves legendary status – as in traditional tales – it becomes a pool of active wisdom ready to be harvested.

Story practitioners are adept at this.

As Alida Gersie explains (Gersie, 1997), traditional tales can be used creatively within groups of individuals to:

- Help a capacity for relationship to flourish;
- Clarify disturbed thoughts and feelings;
- Work through troubling memories towards re-interpretation;
- Improve their self-narratives through self-reflection; and
- Open up future possibilities.

Using Story to achieve these outcomes is a fruitful strategy in health and social care situations and this has become a major plank in my own practice. This is how it works.

When facilitating a Story workshop, I begin by filling the room with flowers, art materials, and photos or pictures relating to the theme of the story I've chosen to share. I also choose some appropriate music. For example, to set the scene and mood for the story of the Seal Wife (see below), I use a Hebridean song produced by Scottish folk musicians Capercaille.

Group members must feel safe before they consent to participate fully, and, I find, establishing consensus on confidentiality helps. (I use the Chatham House rule: "What is said in the room stays in the room".) But, as facilitator, I also try to create an encouraging atmosphere. Self-disclosure happens during all workshops – which can be difficult for some participants. Vocal and judgmental group members – who feel they know best – must learn from the outset they will not be given the floor exclusively.

This approach maximises the value of group membership. As Alida Gersie explains:

- Each values the help each offers – for example, during a discussion of practical coping mechanisms;

- Group members respond to the individual's story – they bear witness, they hold accountable, and they remember what has been said;

- Improved relationships arise from shared responses (and the common humanity underlying them).

And, when the appropriate atmosphere has been established, I can then tell the story.

The stories I choose come from many sources – fairy and folk tales, personal anecdotes, films, books, and songs. As humans, we share common hopes, fears and value systems with people from all over the world and throughout history – generating a massive resource from which to select relevant materials.

Sometimes I read a story (tapping into the individual's memories of being read to). Sometimes I speak it. Either way, the group/audience is now focused – because stories engage them and they want to know what happens next. They listen attentively.

Box 1 – The Story

The Seal Wife – a traditional Hebridean Tale, retold by Elizabeth Gates

Every year, on the Isle of Berneray, for one day only, young selkies leave the sea. And once upon a time, when I was the most beautiful of all my sisters, I longed to dance as others had at the Water's Edge.

The Year passed. The Day came. We hauled ourselves out of the turquoise sea and slid from our skins. The pile of our pelts grew - black, white, silver, dark brown. And mine, glimmering gold in the sun.

And then, my children, oh how we danced, I and the Prince of Seals – the most handsome and the strongest of his generation. On sands white as silver against clouds black as peat. Love filled our world.

But, oh, my children – now I must tell you the story of how I almost lost you. And of another grief which came to me instead.

The Day was over. My sisters, my brothers, laughing, pulled their skins from the pile and plunged again into the welcoming sea. But I wept. My brothers and sisters were gone and I was alone. My beautiful golden skin – it was nowhere to be found. And, without it, I could not return to the sea. And the Prince of Seals was calling me – across the waves of the evening sea. His call was lonely. It echoed the loneliness of my own heart. I thought my heart would break.

Then, I realised, I would have to find my pelt myself.

Across the green mounds behind the strand, I could smell a peat fire. And, I was sure, my pelt was somewhere near that fire. I followed the peat scent on the air – smoking, bitter, ancient. Salt in the wind.

My legs pained me to walk. Magic was dying with the Sun. The sea was black. The world was suddenly cold. Suddenly hostile. And I was facing nothing I had ever known.

Then, outlined against the firelight, I saw him. A fisherman, hulked in the darkness, listening to my weeping. "Man!" I cried, "Man! If you have my pelt, please give it back. Without it, I cannot go home."

The fisherman did not give me my skin. But he led me to his hearth, to his peat fireside, and warmed me with cloth woven from the wool of sheep tended on the Isles and dyed with the berries and flowers and lichens of the Isles' earth and washed with the rain of the Isles' heaven.

I was enchanted. And I stayed. And I bore him a daughter. A beautiful child – entirely perfect – even down to the webs of skin between her tiny fingers and toes. She was so beautiful, your sister. It broke my heart to leave her.

But leave her I did.

It happened this way. I loved the fisherman. In my way. I tended him. I tended his croft. Though I could not forget that I did not belong. And I continued to search long after I had forgotten what I searched for.

Then one day I saw something hidden up in the thatch – gleaming gold in the firelight, concealed by the fisherman's hand. What I had searched for – all that time – had found me. It was time to go.

At first, I didn't understand what choice lay before me. But I was compelled to choose. I kissed my darling child, thinking I would see her with the returning sun. I ran again to the shore, across the silver sand and down to the turquoise sea. I drew on my golden pelt, dived from the rocks into the deep and gleaming water and swam towards the setting sun.

As I swam, I became aware of a seal swimming alongside me. It was the Prince of Seals. And now we could dance again. We reclaimed ourselves – and our sea – and he became your father. And I never went back again to walk on the land.

But, I do sometimes swim near Berneray again. And she walks there. And I call to her. She hears the longing in my call. But she does not understand. I call and I call my love to her but she does not understand...

The group is then invited to respond to prompts designed to explore issues raised. Writing exercises are used to trigger awareness of patterns and contrasts within their own life for each individual. [Box 2]

Box 2 – Possible creative writing prompts

- Which is the most significant moment for you in this story? What are the images, sounds, scents, textures, tastes, feelings you noted at that moment?

- Explore your happy memories. Compare and contrast Berneray with your own life. Create a written picture of somewhere you would love to return to.

- Change the story of the Seal Wife. Write a poem or a piece of prose or dialogue as if by the seal children. Or the human child. Think why you want to change the story and understand how. Then create a different ending.

Group members are then invited to share their learnings with a partner or – if they wish – with the whole group. [Box 3]

Box 3 – Possible prompts for discussion

- What are the moral issues of this story? This story is told from the viewpoint of the Seal Wife. Usually, in the Hebrides, it is told from the viewpoint of the fisherman. How would this alter the moral issues? Discuss with a partner

- Loneliness – when have you felt lonely? Where is the loneliest place you have been to? Tell a partner. Listen to their story.

- What do you want to share with the whole group?

Issues raised by a story may relate to sickness or may have some other significance. For example, the story of the Seal Wife deals – in part – with loneliness. Composed perhaps of patients who live alone, isolated carers or the parents of sick children, for example, a group can and does respond strongly to this theme. In my experience, group members, identify immediately with someone in the wrong place at the wrong time who wants to return to their own fold and they understand fully the emotional costs and implications of this. Value systems also come under challenge.

Any session must be concluded with a debriefing. Unresolved concerns must, at least, be acknowledged.

Story cannot cure serious illness or injury but it can promote wellbeing and there can be therapeutic benefits in this. If you are tempted to explore the possibilities of story-sharing in healthcare, the resources referred to in this chapter and listed in the references could help you to get you started.

And, if you have further questions, please see my story-telling and writing for wellbeing website – http://lightforshadows.wordpress.com or email me directly: elizabeth@lonelyfurrowcompany.com.

References

Charon, R. (2008). *Narrative medicine – honoring the stories of illness.* USA: OUP.

Frank, A. W. (1995). *The wounded storyteller: Body, illness and ethics.* USA: University of Chicago Press.

Frank, A. W. (2010). *Letting stories breathe: A socio-narratology.* USA: University of Chicago Press.

Gersie, A. (1997). *Reflections on therapeutic story-making: Like a piece of uncast wood.* London: Jessica Kingsley.
Only Human Communication. (2012). *Bringing out the best in people.* Retrieved 4 March 2012 from http://www.onlyhuman.com.au/

Sayer-Jones, M. 2006. *In my life.* Australia: Only Human Communication http://www.onlyhuman.com.au/

An Advent Story by Jill Goulden

It was a cold wintry evening, just before Christmas in 2005. I was half listening to Radio Cumbria while I contemplated the supper dishes in the sink.

Then the sometimes banal waffle was interrupted by a new voice. An excited voice, a compelling voice, inviting listeners to pull back the curtains and look outside. The speaker, an amateur astronomer, was watching the sky from the grounds of Kendal Castle. "Look at the western sky," he said. "Look at the moon!"

I switched off the light behind me and the gazed out into the darkness. Sure enough, there was the moon – a perfect pale yellow crescent, lying low in the western sky. I could see Venus shining above it, but then there was something else – the pattern looked wrong. There was a very bright star close to the tip of the crescent moon, and sparkling with a very intense light in the calm night sky.

"And that," said the radio presenter, "is the Space Station!" I suppose they were millions of miles apart, but the juxtaposition of the lemon segment of the ancient moon and the blatant clarity of the very modern spaceship was extraordinary.

It was travelling but I could scarcely discern the movement: there were men in that machine, controlling it and exploring the vast spaces of the sky. I wondered what the man in the moon would make of the upstart!

Just a moment in time for me – the earth and the sky connected so vividly. As I stood looking out of the window, I couldn't help remembering those Three Wise Men, following their bright star to Bethlehem.

A Picture of Health by Steve Childerley

To Keep yourself fit, exercise, don't just sit,
Whenever you've time for a break.
To keep your weight down, take a walk around town,
And a healthy example you'll make.

Eat plenty of greens, like sprouts, runner beans,
Have skimmed milk and fruit for a snack.
You'll be kind to your teeth and those gums underneath,
And you'll gain all those vitamins you lack.

And of course, never smoke, unlike some silly folk,
Who cough and splutter and wheeze.
And stay off those drugs, they're only for mugs,
You'll find your life more of a breeze.

If you **must** have a vice, try yoga, it's nice,
It strengthens your body and mind.
At the end of the day, you'll relax in a way,
That will leave all those troubles behind.

So for happy, long living, just think about giving
Your body the care it may crave.
Stay healthy and trim, and you'll feel much less grim,
And you won't go so soon, to your grave!

Chapter 11 – Writing Myself

A personal account of using writing in recovery from head injury.

John Berry

Waking up in hospital

My first recollection was of waking up in hospital with no idea of how I got there or why. I had no memory of my accident or of 'real life'. Reality and dream state became all jumbled.

In my next recollection I was sitting in a train waiting for an ambulance to come. But when the ambulance turned up and I was being moved by the orderly, I was very confused by the fact that there was no sign of the train I believed I had been sitting in.

I can remember travelling in an ambulance towards Carlisle, and my thoughts became more 'normal' from this point on. But my memory was still shot with holes and I was remembering a strange dream state I had been through as if it was real. I had difficulty separating the fiction from reality.

Once I arrived in Carlisle I remember having my ankle 'sorted out' and various pins and dressings removed before a plaster cast was applied. Once I was in bed in a ward I was visited by a specialist who asked questions I had great difficulty answering due to a loss of memory and speech. This left me surprised and confused.

My wife Louise came to see me and at this stage my mind was still a blank about my accident. I was also still confused about a period of time I had apparently spent in hospital in Preston before being transferred to Carlisle. Louise told me about my accident and my rescue by helicopter. She told me that I was taken to Preston first, and transferred from one helicopter to another, and then one hospital to another. I had no memory of any of it. My thoughts and memory and basic understanding were very fuzzy and I forgot things from one day to another. So it was over a month before the facts of my accident, my helicopter trips, my time in Preston hospital, etc., became apparent to me.

Slowly I started to readjust and separate the weird dream state of Preston from the realities explained to me by Louise. Contrary to my false memories, I was never in a train, nor was I taken to a hospital in Penrith as I had thought. I had memory of my ambulance journey but no memory about the helicopter trips. My time spent in the hospital in Preston was not as I thought just a short day or night, but several days spent in unconsciousness – none of which naturally I had any memory of. The fact that I had been on a climbing trip when my accident occurred and had fallen a considerable distance with my leg tangled round the rope, breaking various bones, including my skull, came as a complete surprise. I had no recollection of my climbing trip, no memory of my fall, and could not even remember the person I had been climbing with.

Speech and memory now became a problem. Visits to the hospital from friends and relatives were difficult because although I knew I knew them, I could not remember names or the words to use when speaking to them. I was surprised and thankful for all the visits and the concern showed by them. But I also felt rather foolish because the reason I was there was probably a mistake I made when climbing.

After I had been in hospital for some time I assumed I would be going home soon. But as time went on and no one told me if or when I was to leave, I became unsure as to what exactly was the problem with me. The nurses and ward staff were very good to me but being stuck in hospital doing nothing for days on end was disconcerting and left me bored.

The first idea I had was to ask Louise to bring me some books to read, but this proved to be very difficult for me. Reading a novel was impossible for me as I simply forgot what I read within minutes of reading it and had difficulty discerning one passage from the next. This was another big surprise because reading was something I did a lot of prior to my accident. A short limp down the hospital corridor with the aid of a walking frame meant I could visit a patients' library. In the library I discovered and borrowed a children's book by Enid Blyton. I found I could manage to read children's books with less of a problem; though I could only manage a page or two at a time with many memory gaps and repeated forgotten paragraphs. I knew I had read the books as a child, but I could in no way remember the stories.

After quite a few weeks I had the pot removed from my broken left leg and my swollen and battered ankle was a huge and disconcerting sight to me, which brought on a fear of how this was going to end up and if I would ever become in any way 'normal' again. Then the first pot was replaced by another and I was left worrying about my future ability (or disability) to walk.

Home at last

A whole month went by in the hospital at Carlisle before I was finally allowed to go home, and only then after the consultants had visited the house to ensure I would be able to manage and that I would be looked after by Louise.

At first I thought I would be pleased and relieved to be home. I expected life to become more normal and easy to handle. I was wrong. It was harder to organise myself at home than it was in hospital, and using my brain was difficult for anything for more than short spells, either for thought, speech or actions. When I wanted to read I could only manage a few pages at a time. When I wanted to talk my speech was completely jumbled and the words hard to remember. When I moved I became disorientated and often lost my balance. The first luxury of being back at home was a bath, which I managed by keeping my swollen left ankle out of the water.

After a while I was able to go back to sleeping in the bedroom and I learned to take enough care when moving about to prevent myself from falling over. The most difficult thing was the speech problem. When trying to converse with visiting family or friends, the more animated the conversation the harder it became to remember the words to use. Memory was also a big problem when I tried to recall the names of people and places. Friends and family were good about waiting for my speech to arrange itself, and didn't laugh too much when my words became too jumbled, especially when I got their names wrong!

I started to have home visits from specialists such as speech therapists and occupational therapists. Later I became aware that these therapists were from the brain trauma department of the Carleton Clinic. I found the term brain trauma very disconcerting at first.

A visit from my speech therapist was now occurring approximately weekly. At first I thought I was doing well when talking to her, until she told me about all the mistakes I made and the wrong words I used because I couldn't remember the right words. An occupational therapist was also visiting weekly and we discussed my problems with pain in my arms, and unsteadiness, together with a feeling of disorientation and fatigue from the smallest amount of concentration. He came up with many ideas for ways I could help myself improve. Like making notes from period to period or day to day, organising myself to do certain tasks in short spells with rests between them, and changing between physical tasks and mental tasks when they became tiring.

Writing as a tool

One of the main problems arising from the therapists' ideas was their suggestion about writing things down, e.g., notes to myself, writing down recipes when cooking, keeping a diary, or a weekly plan of my actions. To write using pen and paper was a problem: the damage to my right hand meant that my writing was almost illegible and my hand soon started aching. However the help that writing provided to my thought processes was tremendous because I found it easier to read what I had written than to try to remember something I had done or said previously without having the writing to remind me. On the one hand writing gave me a big advantage by enabling me to read my own written words and thoughts, but on the other hand there was the physical problem of writing with my damaged hand.

When I first arrived home from the hospital I sat down and switched on my computer. As a working man, using the computer had been a daily occurrence and I naturally thought nothing of using it – until I switched it on and found I couldn't remember the simplest thing about using it. Even so I found I was able to use it to write, even though I had all but forgotten how to type. My speech therapist emailed me with a suggested method of keeping a weekly plan. At first my wife printed this out and I had the same old problem of writing by hand. So I started to fill in the emailed form on the computer and suddenly there was no stopping me as I found writing with the computer much easier than trying to write by hand.

The problems I had with my memory of words, and the speech problems this engendered, were of little hindrance to writing because when I couldn't find a word from memory it didn't matter that it took me some time to bring it to mind. When talking to people my speech and memory were constant problems, but when writing I could take all the time needed to think of what to say.

Suddenly I had the idea of writing about my memories of childhood and the more I thought about my childhood, the more memories that I didn't even realise I had kept springing to mind. Writing memories like these were of importance only to me. It did not matter if no-one else ever read or understood what I was writing about. I found that the more I immersed myself in the thought and typing process the easier it became to use my brain in the slower and disjointed way that made conversation with people so impossible. However the use of my brain when writing proved to be very difficult when noises or other distractions were going on in the background, such as the radio, TV or just other people talking amongst themselves. Getting out of bed in the early hours and sitting at the computer to type in comparative quiet was much better and I started to write about my childhood memories with greater ease.

Memories of Jarrow

"Will you get up? You've got school this morning."

Mother threw back the blankets and there was no choice but to get out of bed and get dressed in my clothes for school. Mam made me have a quick breakfast, because she said I was late in getting out of bed, and we set off walking to school along the streets of Jarrow. We walked under the railway bridge, which had a walkway so the cars wouldn't hit anyone, then set off up the hill towards the school.

"Mam that's a double decker," I pointed at the bus heading towards us. We stared as the bus slammed into the low arch of the railway bridge. I thought this very funny as the top of the bus crumpled in and the bus stopped, while the conductor, who was standing in the aisle of the bus, fell flat on his face.

"Don't laugh. Someone might be hurt." Then a smack from my Mam, but it didn't hurt. No one else saw the funny side and lots of people rushed to the bus to help. I thought it lucky that there were no passengers on the bus.

Mother dragged me around and off to school and told me off for finding it funny. I wondered if the driver was hurt and decided that he would get told off too because double deckers couldn't go under the bridge.

I rushed into the school yard and told loads of my mates about the morning bus crash. They were jealous, and they also found it funny when I told them about the conductor falling flat on his face.

We all lined up and trooped into school to Mr Harding's class. We stood up when the teacher came in and chanted "Good morning Mr. Harding." Then we were supposed to sit down again, but the seat was like a form in front of the desks which folded up and down and someone folded it up and half of us ended up sitting on the floor. Mr. Harding glared at us whilst those of us who didn't fall on the floor couldn't stop laughing.

On the way home from school I passed a car with a boot full of rolls of carpets and lino and stuff. I could see right down the centre of them because they had card centres. I walked past the town hall and jumped off and on the kerb by the front of it because it was quite high there.

I went into the house by our back yard, I could see my dad was still working in the bake house. I got in and told my mam I was home and went upstairs to play in my bedroom.

"John come down here," I heard Mam's yell up the stairs so I ran back down to where she stood at the open front door. A policeman was standing at the door telling Mam tales about me doing naughty things on the way home All about me looking in the boot of a car and jumping on and off the kerb, which apparently had frightened a motorist into thinking he was going to hit me. I went back up to my room after the usual telling off from my Mam and wondered what all the fuss was about.

Later on after dinner, my Dad asked me if I wanted to go for a walk with him. This was great because I had never gone out in the dark before. We went out the back way and walked up past the picture place and the sweet shop. Dad bought me some peanut brittle which was sticky and tough and lasted ages. We walked up Ferry Street past the bomb sites, which he told me were from the bombing in the war. They were great big bare patches where buildings had been demolished. They were great places to play on, but I didn't tell my Dad that because it probably wasn't allowed. Dad stood about a lot and talked to people he recognised. He said they were mostly customers in his shop. I didn't know anyone but it was good standing under the streetlamps watching everyone rushing about. I wondered where they were all going.

Writing for pleasure

Whilst my thoughts and memories of the near past and even sometimes from day to day were still a great problem, I found recollections of childhood days were coming much easier and sometimes with greater enjoyment than I would ever have thought. Using my brain, whilst a great problem on a daily basis, suddenly became an enjoyable exercise. It mattered not what thoughts or memories, of what or when, came to me when writing. Nor did it matter whether anyone read my writing, or liked what they read. Writing became a personal thing which meant that the use of my brain, normally a great problem, became much more fulfilling. Childhood memories led on to other memories, all disjointed, from all different parts of my life: school, work, successes, failures, all kinds of everything. Writing became a great way I could express myself to myself and having the written words to read meant memory lapses were more easily recovered from my written words.

I still have great holes in my memory of the things pertinent to my accident and life in general, but the memories brought to the fore by the continued writing have made life so much better and more bearable.

During the time I spent in hospital after my accident the care and attention given by the doctors and nurses was wonderful, as was the help I received from the therapists from the Carleton Clinic. My near death accident and the brain trauma caused was a continual annoyance to me, especially the problems of speech and memory, but I suddenly found that being able to write was a huge benefit both for my speech and memory problems and for myself.

Moving on

With my busy life in business left behind me after the accident, I became semi-retired. I spent most of my time at home doing little or nothing, reading, television and even doing housework just to occupy myself. With nothing much else to do I started to eat too much and drink too much coffee and even developed a paunch! Never being one to exercise in a gym, or similar, I decided to take up walking in the Lakes for reasons of rebuilding my health.

Taking up walking has led on to a new project: I have started writing about my walks and am planning to write a book. A lot of books about walking in the Lakes are for the extremely fit, wishing to scale the heights or mountain tops. I write about long gentle rambles, with just a little uphill walking. I now leave the mountain tops to others.

The Wedding Album by Judy Gray

It was such a beautiful day;
the air was full of happiness and love
the church bells sang out over the town –
a perfect wedding
such joy.

I sit now, the wedding album on my knee
not knowing whether to
unleash those memories
or keep them locked away
in the box.

Shall I burn it and all the memories it holds?
shall I keep it for future generations to see
and maybe understand what went wrong?
shall I hide it away in the attic as if the day
never happened?

Photographs recalling happy days are treasured forever
but what of those that bring deep sadness to the heart?
they are, after all, part of life's journey
to be reflected upon sometime in the future ....
but not yet.

It WAS such a beautiful day.

Love by Alison Gawne

Love is my children, love is Alfie, love is the man who will protect, cherish and die for you.
Love is the world, the flowers, the butterflies, the beauty of the world.
Love is pure, love is simple. Love is everything you need.
Love is a happy, joyous, adventurous, easy thing to do. Love happens when you least expect it.
 Love is pure, love is simple, without love there is nothing.
Love is a rainbow. Somewhere over the rainbow, love is everywhere.

Chapter 12 – Another Door Opens

Suzanne Kelsey

A door slammed in my face
I found myself in a temporary 'No man's land.'
Isolated, lonely and vulnerable
I stared at the closed door
Longing to go back
Sadness, fear, anger starting to take over
Deep inside I knew I had to go forward
I turned to face a new door
It slowly opened before me
I was brave and crossed the threshold
I found new places, new people and new experiences
My life enriched by
Connecting
Giving
Rediscovering
Catching sight of the beautiful.

One of my mother's favourite sayings was, "When one door closes another door opens" (Alexander Graham Bell).

I realised that this famous quote was her way of delivering in a very simplistic way a profound message that would subtly prepare my young developing mind for the disappointments, upsets, and major changes as well as the sheer joy that life would inevitably bring. It became a guiding principle in my life and part of my own personal philosophy applying it to challenging situations that are all part of the human condition. In 2009 this abiding theory was certainly put to the test.

I had always been very fit and proactive in my efforts to lead a healthy lifestyle. I was a trained teacher specialising in dance and drama, dance trained at the Laban dance studios in London, a qualified health and fitness instructor and a tutor on the 'Look After Your Heart' programme, as well as a full-time teacher and lecturer in education and child development.

Imagine my horror when I suddenly collapsed, my heart going into bizarre and alarming rhythms. I was diagnosed with heart failure and a chronic condition called cardiomyopathy caused by a virus. I was in a state of shock. When diagnosed with a chronic and/or acute illness the psychological effect can be as traumatic as the physical threat. I experienced a maelstrom of emotions. Initially I was in denial, fearful about my expected future, sad and at times downright angry that all my best efforts to remain fit and healthy had somehow failed.

Fortunately I had exemplary care from a very dedicated cardiologist and her team at the Cumberland Infirmary. It was of some comfort to me that I knew I was in very safe hands.

When I was recuperating, having had to give up my dance and fitness regime to rest my heart, I instinctively knew once over the initial crisis I needed an outer focus to prevent being caught up in a spiral of negative emotions that could lead to depression.

I needed to restore my self-worth that in an instant had been stolen from me. I wanted to engage with something purposeful that would benefit me and hopefully others.

To show my gratitude for the wonderful care I was receiving from the Cardiology Department at the Cumberland Infirmary I decided to do some fund raising for them. My initial efforts from a sponsored walk, gift stalls, and a quiz raised £1,250. At the same time I had returned to my love of poetry for relaxation and comfort.

I had often used words in my choreography because of the rhythm, musicality and symbolism, although I hasten to add I had never taken a class in creative writing. I already had a small private collection of my poetry, so I started to organise this, which motivated me into writing more, reflecting on recent events.

A Stranger Came to Stay

Quite unexpectedly a stranger came to stay with me.
This was a malicious stranger whom I knew wanted to hurt me.
I was frightened and upset.

I became brave and looked this stranger in the eye. "Why have you come here uninvited?" I asked.

The stranger could not give me an explanation but said,
"My name is Cardio Myopathy and I am going to live in your soul deep inside your heart".

I was even more afraid as I did not want a stranger knowing the secrets of my inner being.

So I started my quest for some answers about this stranger and their intentions.

I found a cardiologist whom I trust and respect, she is an expert in affairs of the heart.

She showed such care and concern and gave me a prognosis to protect my heart.

My partner and family did not want an introduction to this stranger and chose to ignore their presence, hoping they would go away as quickly as they came so my heart could be in their safe keeping again.

My beautiful Goddaughter, who nurtures the spirit gave me her healing hands to hold, to restore my heart.

My dear friends took me away from this stranger.

They made me laugh and forget that the stranger was there still waiting, sinister and pernicious

My friends would revive my heart.

At first I left this stranger alone and isolated.

I became angry for Cardio Myopathy would not go away.

Being compassionate I later asked the stranger to accompany me.

Seeking enlightenment for my body, mind and spirit.

During this time when we established a relationship, we were able to be honest with each other.

The stranger confessed that they had come to warn me.

To make me aware that my heart needed help.

During this journey I would find many people who would restore my belief in mankind.

I had always great faith in humanity and this would remind me why.

It would rekindle my spiritualism and self affirmation.

Slowly, slowly I felt my heart was starting to heal, my soul was being renewed.

Together we can begin to repair the damage that is done by a cruel virus that crept upon me one starless night when I was sleeping.
So it seems, me and that stranger Cardio Myopathy have become good friends, for now I understand.

There is increasing recognition of the healing power of poetry. It fills the space between our thoughts and experiences and for me during this time of recuperation the words seemed to be coming directly from the soul; another door had definitely been opened wide.

The poems were coming thick and fast and so another idea started to evolve that perhaps I could use my poems to raise further money for the hospital and to provide comfort to others. I had never put my poetry out there in the public arena apart from writing and reciting humorous poems for certain people and on special occasions. So I sought the advice of friends who were given the poetry to read and comment on. It was their positive reinforcement that gave me the confidence to publish them.

What started as an acorn grew into a mighty oak and on July 16th 2010 I launched my first poetry book called *Echoes* with a party for over 70 invited guests. I have had a busy year marketing this book and at the time of writing I have raised over £2,500 from the sales. The book derived its title from the **Echo**cardiogram that initially diagnosed my heart condition, hence this signature poem from the book.

Echoes

Shadowy, magnificent shapes brooding in the distance.
Embraced by phantom mists rising from the deep.
Echoes of ancient times – ancient times
When life on earth was pure and balanced
The reverberating roar of silence
Becomes deafening to the soul
Interrupted only by the gentle, constant
Wave upon wave flowing to the lake shore

Reflecting the mood of the moon and stars
As if time stood still in this place
Long before man's breath touched the emptiness
And filled the void with chaos
Desolation and wonder
Walking hand in hand
Mother Earth's cries echo far away – far away
If we listen carefully we can rescue her broken heart.

The poetry book opened other new doors as I have been invited to give talks to various support groups locally, whom I hope, despite their various chronic or acute illnesses, have been motivated to read and write poetry as a therapy.

I strongly believe in integrative medicine with its holistic approach to good health and healing. It draws on other cultures to treat the mind, body and spirit and in my opinion can help to heal the body by promoting a mental positive attitude, so I also pursued other complementary therapies that I thought would help me. I took up tai chi, shiatsu, meditation and guided imagery; I started to give my heart some tender loving care, and stopped to smell the flowers. All of these activities seemed to open up my heart and soul and the creative process continued to flow.

On a visit to the Lake District, inspired by the beauty that surrounded me I wrote profusely. No wonder the Lakes poets, Wordsworth, Southey and Coleridge were part of the Romantic Movement and were so prolific! Here are two of the six I wrote over a few days stay there.

Solitude

Through the early morning mist
On a tranquil lake
A solitary shadowy figure appears
Lost in the solitude of this new day
With its promise of a maturing sun
This is the perfect golden time to reflect.
In the ripples of a silver shimmer
Emerge images of childhood memories.

Those long hot sunny days stretching before us
The sweet fragrance of summer
Sensed even before waking.
Faces of people that have come into our lives
When we needed them the most.
Echoing voices of friends that have stayed
To affirm who we are and who we want to be.
Feeling the touch of loves lost and loves found
All shaped who we are today.
Relationships are necessary
Solitude is needed
Giving us time to be grateful for what we have.

Come Dance with Me

Come dance with me my friend
Through the purple mists of time
Dancing for yesterday, today and tomorrow.
Dance with me like the gentle breeze
That will blow away your pain
Dancing to heal the mind.
Dance with me
Ebbing to and fro
Dancing to restore the spirit.
Dance with me
Towards the sun with fire in your heart
Dancing to nourish the soul.
Dance with me around the world
Holding hands with those we meet
Dancing to love.
Dance with me from dusk to dawn
Moving from darkness into light

Dancing forever.

I also left my poetry books for people to read in waiting rooms, at the dentist, the GP's surgery and the hospital. I was more than delighted when I started receiving feedback from leaving them in these places. A vicar contacted me and asked if she could use them in her work, a grandmother asked if she could use one at her grandchild's christening, a lady got in touch with me who also writes poetry to tell me she found 'Come dance with me' particularly powerful. Many people have many different favourites and I was so pleased about this. I was achieving one of my goals, I was reaching out to a wide audience, there was a poem for everyone.

Through my poetry and all of the activities I had now become involved in I was meeting new people, visiting new places and thoroughly enjoying new experiences. It is so true therefore that poetry can connect us with others, hopefully in friendship, sometimes in love and always in better understanding.

This further motivated me into writing a second book called *Threads*. The poems reflect significant events in the common threads of life. I dedicated this to my late parents and it was to be given to family and close friends as a thank you for their unerring support and generosity during my illness and fundraising.

Threads of Friendship

I have collected a different coloured thread
From every stranger I have met
Each stranger becoming a friend
Each friend a special gift to me
I will weave them all together
Make a blanket of comfort
Wrap myself in it
When I need to feel secure
Display the colours and patterns
For all to see the beauty in the threads of friendship.

Threads of Revelation

Follow the continuous threads of revelation
Hold on to them as they unfold in the silent darkness
When the inner eye truly starts to see
All that can now be safely revealed
To satisfy the hungry soul
Through the stillness and quiet
Uninterrupted by the harsh light of the day

Journey on a whisper of spiritual dreams
Allow the invisible threads to travel towards like minds
Feel privileged to be part of their very being
Connect in meaningful ways
Listen intently absorb their words and experiences
Observe their movements and learn their dance steps
Trace their rhythmical pattern wherever they lead
As daylight emerges create a beautiful performance
Choreographed from the continuous threads of revelation
Freely given to you as a gift from those you love.

People often ask me where my ideas come from and the answer of course is from everyday life. The poetry I write can be based on the more serious observations of life but also on anecdotal humour and for some reason I tend to write the latter in rhyming couplets. It seems somehow that the contrived, obvious and artificial rhyming of the words adds to the humorous images I want to portray. Every situation I find myself in can inspire me to start writing, even overheard conversations. Friends are becoming a little wary when talking to me and often fall silent when I suddenly take out my little poetry notebook and start scribbling furiously! As part of my recuperation I attended cardiac rehabilitation and just before I left I wrote this poem for the hospital staff as a thank you for their care and compassion.

Rehabilitation Threads

There is a team of lasses working down in cardio rehab
Who deserve a lot of praise 'cos they are really quite 'Ab Fab'!
They work together so efficiently complementing each other all the
  time
Listen to the threads of your heart story which is why I am writing
  them this rhyme
I was full of trepidation when I first entered that formidable room
But their cheery friendly faces soon stopped me feeling glum
They will start by checking out your BP and if your little heart races
Instil you with much confidence before they put you through your
  paces.

They gave me a little warm up before I began to pedal

Then set me off on my programme to win an Olympic medal.
Then without much ado they quickly told me "Suzanne get on 'yer
    bike!"
But I wasn't really offended as they treat everyone alike!
There's Judith who demonstrates such care and dedication
Nothing is too much trouble I am so full of admiration.
Barbara with her enthusiasm is most definitely Mrs. Motivator
Who will ensure you reach your HRMax then leave you wanting
    more.

Hazel is so kind and reassuring she always tries to please
Her friendly smiling face always putting you at ease.
Beccy the quiet and younger one is very versatile
She will help you with everything to go that extra mile.
I feel I have been here forever with various setbacks from
    cardiomyopathy
But you have been so patient and understanding so full of sympathy
You really have helped my heart grow stronger in a lot more ways
    than one
I reckon this time next year I will be winning the London Marathon!

The one below was written after a very prolonged telephone call to a utility company. Not exactly Chaucer or Shakespeare but nevertheless very therapeutic!

Vivaldi

I have become an expert on Vivaldi he has become my very best mate
I listen to his music regularly the Four Seasons are just great
It doesn't matter who I ring be it BT, Sky, Tescos or Eon
Vivaldi is always there do they have his PERMISSION?
With all respect dear Vivaldi I no longer want you on my line
Please no more taped music a human voice would be just fine!

It is now over two years since I was diagnosed with cardiomyopathy. I am pleased to report that although my heart is not quite 100%, I am feeling much better. Although 'retired' from education, I am very active and new doors keep opening up. The dedicated care of the hospital personnel and my self-healing therapies have helped enormously.

Two of my poems were selected to be published in a national anthology and I am about to self publish my third book called *Serendipity*, which will again be on sale to raise further funds that are now nearing a total of £4,000.

The word serendipity has always been one of my favourites, the meaning itself is magical "Making fortunate discoveries whilst looking for something unrelated" (Collins, 1999, p. 1353). Serendipity presents us with the foundation for important intellectual leaps of faith. Personally I prefer the interpretation that the existence of serendipity should allow us to think outside the box, avoid bigoted views, promote creativity and encourage forward thinking and most of all live life as an adventure, appreciating its rich diversity.

The *Serendipity* collection is again an eclectic mix of humorous and reflective poetry. It is dedicated to the many people in my life that I profoundly respect, love, admire and cherish. Through them I have gathered the positive energy to continue with my fundraising, voluntary work and creative writing. I have made and met up with new friends both young and old through the Cardiomyopathy Association, one of whom is a fellow poet and story teller. These are incredibly brave and supportive people with whom I have been able to share personal heart stories. I would never have had the privilege to meet them had it not been for my own diagnosis. Encouraged by the cardiac nurses I am currently chairwoman of our local cardiac support group that offers advice, information, social activities and most of all friendship. Without any of this insight, understanding, friendship and kindness I would not have had the self-belief to produce any of these books, thereby making unexpected discoveries about myself and the magical Laws of the Universe. The people and events in my life have therefore become pure moments of **Serendipity.**

I would like to conclude this chapter with a selection of poems taken from this book as they can adequately summarise the well being there is to be had from the power of words.

Serendipity

Seek the answers to find new versions of the truth
Expect the unexpected to open new doors
Reaffirm the existence of the magic all round
Empathise to understand and resolve differences
Nurture young minds about the mysteries that surround them
Discover your own creative potential
Imagine all things are possible
Persuade others to open their minds
Inspire actions for the greater good
Teach the world about Universal Law
You can then achieve SERENDIPITY in your own life.

Recycling Our Lives

I have got to do more recycling or the council will impose a fine
I do not want to break the law and commit such a heinous crime
The only problem is I am utterly confused as to what goes where and
  when
I have the total of six bins that need filling again and again!
I seem to spend my spare time sorting out yogurt pots, glass, card
  and tins
I am really quite fed up having so much to wash and to rinse
I know I will have to get a grip and become familiar with the
  rotations
When the wheelie bins are due out and all the other waste
  collections.

I can feel myself becoming anxious the recycling police are snooping
  around
I have to ensure the bins are out on the correct day no rubbish
  overflowing on the ground.
Maybe we need to bin our emotional constraints, consider recycling
  our own life
Liberate mind and body of meaningless clutter free of unwanted
  stress and strife.
Dump the hurts suffered in the past let go and not allow ourselves to
  ruminate

Make use of the precious moments given to us remain optimistic
and free of hate.
So as we compartmentalise our rubbish throw the unwanted things
away
All negative thoughts in the correct bins let us enjoy our fully
recycled day.

Postcode Lives

Standing on a railway platform in CA1
Observing the anticipation of life
Loved ones part, and new journeys begin
Sad farewells, joyful reunions.
Sitting in a coffee bar in NW3
Observing the rich diversity of life
A multitude of unique faces pass me by
Strangers today, friends tomorrow.
Waiting in a hospital in BR6
Observing the fragility of life
Doctors and nurses reassure anxious souls
Fear alleviated, hope restored.
Relaxing by a lakeside in LA22
Observing the peaceful beauty of life
Reflecting upon the infinite mysteries of our universe
The light and darkness, within and without.

Creativity

Tell me a fable that will never end
Take me to a far off land, absorbing the magic in your words.
Choreograph me a dance that will free the spirit
Take me back in time moving in the now and towards the future.
Write me the words that will connect with my soul
Take me to a new understanding appreciating I am not alone.
Paint me a picture that captures a precious moment, take me into
another world
Opening my eyes to the beauty I can touch.
Compose me a symphony to express my inner most feelings
Take me to the rhythm of my own creativity
Listening to the sound of our universal energy.

I am delighted that I was inspired to return to my love of poetry and subsequently publish my three poetry books. Creative writing has given me a great sense of purpose, helped to ease the restless mind, enabled me to feel positive and restored my feelings of self-worth. It has healed my heart in more ways than one. Expressing my inner feelings has increased my all round sense of wellbeing, my capacity to connect with others, enhanced my life and hopefully the lives of others by sharing the most precious gift of creativity.

> "All who are creative in whatever way are doing something very important to the well being of the world" (Sandra Chantry, cited on Genn, 2012).

References

Genn, R. (2012). *Sandra Chantry art quotes*. Retrieved 5 February 2012 from http://quote.robertgenn.com/auth_search.php?authid =1802

Collins. (1999). *Concise dictionary*. Glasgow: Harper Collins.

First Lapwings by Fernando Smith

Mirror dance
above the
fresh field
Two open
hands behold
the sun
Dry voices
calling out
winter.

Heart Murmurs by Elaine Trevitt

The doctor said "Now take these pills
They'll make you well".

I said I'd rather write some poems
and sat down with my pen.

My pen pulled words as if by magic
straight from my heart

which the stethoscope had missed
when the doctor listened in

because the words had been hidden
by a secret flap of skin

but me, my heart and Pen
knew them better out than in

and turned them into something
far greater than the parts

which, as well as being poems
were a set of healing charts.

"Me" by Declan Hall

I am Declan Hall
I go to Montreal
I go to school
I do my work
Bother nobody at all

I go out for break time
Feeling very glad
Some people are good to me
Some are very bad

I try to make friends with them
But they won't leave me be
I want to be their friends and
They can't even see

Now you know how I feel
I hope you understand
I am willing to forgive you all
And even shake your hand.

The Hospital Visit by Linda M. Hughes

I'm sitting in the waiting room,
   I'm in the comfy chair
Because when I came strolling in
   Nobody else was there.
The waiting room is filling now,
   So many come and go;
But me? Well I'm still sitting here
   And why? I'd like to know.
The stated time has long gone by,
   A tray goes in, with tea.
I'm gasping for a cuppa but
   There isn't one for me.
Why do they call us 'patients'?
   I'm rather at a loss.
For one whole hour has now gone by
   And I am very cross!

 This isn't any good you know –
   I really should be glad
That in our splendid country
   Things aren't so very bad.
Just hours away, by aeroplane,
   No hospitals exist;
No friendly Doctors near at hand
   To place upon their list
The sick, the sad, the suffering,
   Those injured in some war
That folks are always fighting,
   No matter what they're for.
Where people battle problems
   For which they aren't to blame...
Hang on – I think I heard somebody
   Calling out my name!

So, in I go, quite chastened, to hear what is my fate,
and to reflect that, after all, it wasn't long to wait.

Having New Hip Poem by Christopher Pilling

Thanks so much for your wishes and card.
I don't want you thinking my life is hard
but some of the things I've had to do
I wish I could have slept right through!
Pads that take turns to squeeze my calves,
others that reduce my biceps by halves,
nurses who wake me at a quarter to six
just to give me some pills and a quick quick fix
of penicillin, and to push a contraption
in my ear to see my body's reaction
in case I'm too hot with 38.
Can we have some more blood? And feel your heart rate?
Lie flat on your back in this water bed
and don't move. If you raise your head
to ease the pain, your body will keep telling
you to wait till your legs stop swelling.
Long live the end of all blasted piss-pots
and needles – and infantile shots
at walking straight with a wayward zimmer
as your muscles get trimmer and trimmer
again and you're ready for walking sticks
and life's fray and the great new tricks
you may perform on a brand new hip
with a will, if not a hop and a skip,
like a trek over to the kitchen sink
to wash my own pots and pour a strong drink.
Having slept at last on the 18th night
I'm starting to feel that it's turned out right
as rain (Why rain?) and I'm almost ready
for the world again. Yes, I know, take things steady
but you'll manage yourself with no nurse to aid
on the journey that you couldn't have made
before the op – to the fridge for ice-cream.
What a dream!

Bluebell Heaven by Lorraine Gibbard

There it was, boldly and proudly proclaimed.
Bluebell Heaven, up the hill on the left I trudged upwards, already
weary, Lured by the promise, yet sceptical.

I was tired from years of chronic illness, But as I became more
committed to my quest, My steps became surer, firmer.

A trickle of Bluebells marked the boundary I drew excited breath
as the scent grew stronger, Then suddenly, there before my
incredulous eyes Lay a haze of blue which carpeted The contours
of the hillside

I scanned all points of the compass
And beheld a sea of swaying bells..
The blue intensity drew tears.
As I began to believe the beauty I saw.

Reverently I wandered
Thanking God for this sumptuous feast.
My senses drank in sight and smell,
As the sweet fragrance soothed my spirit.

I spent time savouring this gift of peace.
My heart was full.
My fatigue began to melt away as I received Joy and peace in this
place.

Bluebells are fragile delicate emblems
Of the God who loves to heal.
The tranquility of this lovely glade
Made me glad to be alive
A message from heaven was here in the Bluebells

Chapter 13 – Your Life is Precious. It is a Gift.

Eileen O'Reilly

Today I know how privileged I am to be sitting at this desk stone cold sober, writing an article that is going to be published. I am living a life fulfilling dreams and achieving goals that were once out of my reach. My addiction crept up on me. Like a thief in the night it robbed me of my pride, my dignity and stole my most valued possession: my life.

In 1986 I was a struggling alcoholic who dreaded waking up in the morning having to face another day filled with shame, embarrassment, guilt and regret at once again failing to control my alcohol intake. With a gigantic hangover I would fulfil my daily chores and make a vow to myself, "Today I will stay sober," and some days I was successful, but not many.

Over twenty years ago I was drinking to oblivion, pouring extra strong lager and whiskey down my throat to dull the mental and emotional pain I was experiencing at that time. I hadn't told or allowed any person into that part of me that was crying out for help. The reason being I couldn't. I was unable to speak about "times best forgotten." I felt lonely, isolated and abandoned with only myself to deal with the overwhelming, torturous, seemingly never-ending emotional pain which was suffocating me on a daily basis. Even sleep didn't provide me with the necessary respite I so clearly needed. Regular nightmares reliving horrendous childhood memories left me feeling drained and unable to cope with life. So alcohol became my best friend, it deadened my pain as it flowed willingly down my throat.

My mind and my life were a living hell and I thought the only solution was to leave my family. I thought my beautiful children would be better off without me. I was planning to travel to London to live in a hostel, beg on the streets and use the money to feed my addiction. To get away as far as possible, so my children could lead respectable lives and not be ashamed of a mother who got drunk on a regular basis. However, thankfully, fate stepped in and I embarked upon a journey which was about to turn my life around.

It was mid morning when I decided to call on my next door neighbour and friend for a chat. As she was putting the kettle on she very gently spoke the following words "Eileen you've got a problem." Shame, guilt and embarrassment rose from deep within me forming a large, solid lump in my throat. Turning away from her I opened the back door and left.

Returning home I sat in a corner of the living room my arms wrapped tightly around my body trying to hug away the pain that shame and guilt inflicts on its victims. I cried for myself, for my family but most of all for that little girl inside me who had suffered such horrendous life experiences.

When the sobbing ceased and I felt in control I picked up a pen and began to write my feelings onto paper. I wrote to my friend about how ashamed and guilty I felt at drinking to excess. The words and sentences told of the times I wished I could stop pouring alcohol down my throat and how my dream was one day I could give up the booze altogether but I couldn't see that dream ever coming true. Four pages of A4 later, I stopped writing and plucked up the courage to take these sheets to my friend and asked her to please read, then destroy and never discuss. The following day as I opened my back door she was there. I could tell by the compassion and pain in her eyes she had read every word.

Writing my thoughts and feelings about my alcoholic problem and passing them over the fence to my friend became a regular pattern. Eventually the sheets of paper were replaced by a diary filled with despair, but also hope that one day I could conquer my addiction. Each time she returned my diary her eyes told me she had read it and that she believed in me. Through constantly recording my feelings, I found the courage to make a promise to her that I would give up the drink on our weekly social evening out. I did it! I succeeded! Week after week, for one night only, not one drop of alcohol passed my lips. I went out sober and I returned sober! This was the beginning of my journey to sobriety. The diaries became my best friend. I wrote from the heart; poured all my daily feelings onto paper. Eventually over the months I stopped drinking altogether but I didn't stop writing.

Whereas before I was writing and trying to stop drinking, I now found myself writing about my craving for the drink. Each time I craved and felt the need to drive to the nearest off licence, I wrote in my diary until the burning desire for alcohol passed. The diaries continued to be written, my friend continued to read them and pass them back over the fence, and sobriety reigned.

Those alcohol fuelled days are far behind me now, way back in my past. I still write a diary, it is now filled with goals I have achieved and dreams that are waiting to be realised. Do I pass them over the fence? No. I have moved on, but will always remember my special friend who walked with me on my journey to sobriety.

Today I am a qualified Life Coach, Neuro-Linguistic Programming Practitioner and an Inspirational/Motivational Speaker. I have written my autobiography putting closure to my past, learning to 'live in the now' and able to plan for a fantastic future. I have written and had published an article 'Writing saves lives' and am in the process of writing my second book, a follow up from my autobiography.

Throughout my diary writing all those years ago, I read a number of books on positive thinking. These past twelve months I decided to also write a self-help mini-book. I hope you enjoy reading the following extract:

Let your imagination take precedence and picture a deck of cards. These cards represent life. Just for fun we will take diamonds and hearts as winning cards, while clubs and spades are to be avoided at all costs. One or two of them are ok and can still be in a winning hand. Too many and you are on a losing streak. The red cards represent the positive comments you have received throughout your life and the black are the negative. As you look at the diamonds and hearts you read the positive statements on each.

Examples of red cards

King of Diamonds...The world's your oyster.

Queen of Hearts...Never take no for an answer.

3 of Diamonds...I'm having a great day.

Jack of Hearts..."Do or do not. There is no try." Yoda (with apologies to George Lucas).

7 of Diamonds..."The ancestor of every action is a thought." Emerson.

5 of Hearts...The road is smooth. Why do you throw rocks before you?

The black cards hold negative statements.

Examples of black cards

King of Spades...I've been dealt a raw deal in life – the cards are stacked against me.

Queen of Clubs...I have failed so often I've forgotten what it feels like to succeed.

9 of Spades...My parents told me we are a family of losers and I'm no different.

Jack of Clubs...Who do you think you are? Get real your brother is the brainy one in this family, marry a rich man, have his kids and be satisfied.

4 of Spades...For women to succeed in business they need to have a male attitude. If they haven't, they're not going to make it.

3 of Clubs...People like us don't make it, we don't belong in that world.

So the cards have been dealt, and if you're holding a winning hand life is exciting. You've a smile on your face like the cat who has just found the cream. Life is good! Or have you been dealt a lousy hand? Are you afraid to even look because your life has always been a drag? You see it as limping from post to post and then you die? You sit at the card table and immediately you know you've lost so, you throw your cards down and sit back whilst someone else who has been dealt a brilliant hand wins.

Does this sound a bit like you? Could it be your life? Can you hear yourself saying, "Someone else has been dealt the winning hand, it's not fair and I'm out of the game. That's why I don't play because I always get a lousy deal." You walk away disgruntled, downhearted, feeling sorry for yourself and promising never to play cards again. Time passes and then comes another opportunity, another card game and you enter into it knowing you're going to lose and you do.

Am I really hearing you saying, "That's me. I have been dealt a lousy hand and how would you like to be told you're worthless? You'll never make it in life. How would you like to hear those words and worse, as every day you sit in your ivory tower writing your damn book"? Well just for the record I have heard those words myself and that's as much as I am revealing. You know that I turned it around because I wasn't going to let anyone tell me that I was thick and stupid, because I knew better. Something inside me said you are better than that and you know what, I am! I have proved it! Now it's up to you to turn around your life today. This very moment is giving you chances and opportunities to live your life the way you want to.

> "The greatest discovery of my generation is that a human being can alter his life by altering his attitudes" James Williams (1842-1910).

If you do not like the cards you have been given, then give them back to the dealer and choose your own. Yeah you heard me right: choose your own. Now I can hear you say, "Hey hold on a minute you can't just give them back, that's breaking the rules." Yeah you're right, I'm all for breaking the rules as long as it won't harm anyone – a rebel in disguise that's me!

191

So now choose a winning hand, shuffle that pack, take a peek at the cards you want, and change your life. I can almost hear you saying, "It's not as easy as that." Well can you hear me saying: "Yes it is! Come on, choose the cards you want to hold in your hand or carry around in your pocket"?

Ace of Hearts...I am good enough.

King of Diamonds...Where there's a will there's a way.

Jack of Diamonds...Be happy just because you can.

Queen of Hearts...Willingness is the key.

6 of Diamonds..."All great achievements require time." Maya Angelou.

8 of Hearts..."What lies behind us and what lies before us are tiny matters compared to what lies within us" Emerson.

We all have certain rules we adhere to, certain cards that we carry around in our pocket. Rules and beliefs which have governed our lives without us ever questioning them. There is a wonderful story I read somewhere a long time ago about a newly married couple. Every time the eager to please wife cooked a ham shank she cut off four corners before placing it into the pan. This went on for months until one day her new husband asked why she prepared the ham this way. She replied, "Because my mother did." Out of curiosity she phoned mum and asked her why she cut off the corners of the ham. Her mum replied, "So it would fit in the pan." I love that story. It highlights how we do things because we have been shown, or taught, or told to, or think we should.

Well, as responsible adults we are in the prime position to question our beliefs. If they are no longer useful, then let them go and replace them with a positive that works for you. Is it that simple? Maybe, maybe not; you won't know if you don't do it! Let's take a negative belief that is holding you back: the **9 of clubs...You're not good enough.** How are you going to get rid of that card? Give it back to the dealer and choose the **Ace of hearts...I am good enough.** Is that it? Is that going to change my life? Yes, if you treat the red card the same way you've treated the black by telling yourself every day that you **are** good enough.

Now is a new beginning and as with most new beginnings they are a little bit scary and exciting. Enjoy hearing the words, "You are good enough!" Write it on an index card, see it, feel it and immerse yourself in it. Will you stop insisting it's not that easy? You believed you weren't good enough! How did you do that? By practising it, by telling yourself over and over again you weren't good enough. You made yourself believe it, now turn it around!! You are good enough, you are good enough. Repeat it after me, "I am good enough!" You're getting there. You'll do it! I know you will because you have all the resources you need to succeed.

How do I think positively and stay positive? How do I 'live life' instead of 'getting through it'?

Practise, practise, practise is the answer and you have all the time in the world to practise because as each day dawns it presents you with the opportunities to PRACTISE. This is where the fun starts.

From the moment you open your eyes in the morning, to the time you fall to sleep at night, for the next seven days I am asking you to be aware of all the opportunities that arise where you can play the game of, **practise, practise and practise.** This may sound strange; you may even be thinking, "how is this going to work?" Well, I'll tell you this is no different than what you have been doing all your life, from the day you were born you have been practising being you. Go back to when you went from lying down to sitting up, from sitting on the carpet to crawling, then walking to running. You had to practise to achieve this and with support you did.

Another example is learning to drive a car. If you've learned to drive you probably got it wrong lots of times at first. Remembering to engage the clutch at the same time as using the gear was an ordeal. There will probably have been times when you wanted to give up, pack it in. So what happened to change your way of thinking? The thought that passing my driving test will change my life and I will become more independent. I will have achieved something equivalent to a rite of passage. Wow I've done it and my life will be easier, I no longer have to rely on others to drive me to my chosen destinations. How cool is that? Well it's the same with practising positive thinking. The more you practise, the easier it gets. The longer you work on yourself, the easier life becomes. Letting go of the way you have been trained to think is liberating; believe me I know. Practise, practise, practise is the key to achievement. Let's take another step forward.

How do I get in touch with my inner resources?

You get in touch with them by knowing they are already there. You don't have to go looking for them, they have always been there from birth and the evidence is staring right at you. Self-motivation, determination, perseverance and resilience, are the foundation stones to a success story. You have always had these resources. I will give you an example of a time when you used all these in one day. Take yourself back to when you were learning to walk. Yep you've got it, I knew you would. All those resources were needed to get you on your feet and moving. Hey I can hear you say you are making assumptions, I can walk. Well hold on; I was just about to give further examples of how these resources come into your everyday life. You don't even think about them because you have been doing them for so long they are as natural as breathing.

Further examples

Getting up in the morning is self-motivation. Waiting to cross a busy road when you're in a hurry is perseverance. Finishing what seems to be an endless task is determination. Going back and doing it again is resilience. Approaching the task in the first place is...yes we're back to it again: self-motivation!

If you've passed your driving test, you needed determination to succeed. The perseverance to continue learning. The resilience to keep trying when you thought you would never get the hang of clutch control. The self-motivation to sit in that driving seat in the first place!

I will leave you with these few words: remember life is precious. It is a gift. Live it, love it and know that you have all the resources inside you to succeed.

Weary Worker by Colin Bentham

I wrote the following several years ago when I looked after my Dad. We had a constant procession of Carers, Nurses, Doctors and others in the house on a daily basis. I don't pretend to be a poet, but just did it as a bit of fun for them.

A nurse's life is oh such fun,
up and down the wards you run.
day and night its all the same,
and all without a hint of fame.

you work so hard and undermanned,
for patients service they demand.
without so much as please or thanks,
its what's expected from the ranks.

but still each day you come for more,
for all the ills you keep no score.
you toil away at what you do,
as this can be done by oh so few.

and when you've finally done your shift,
reaching home is such a gift.
some would say that your cream crackered,
But you know you're just bloody Knackered!

Autumn Leaves by the Autumn Leaves Day Care Group

When October calls those autumn leaves
Flutter by me. Yellow, red and golden,
Falling slowly. Matured with time.
Looking older, wiser. Mellowed with age
But still sparkling in the sun
Swirling in the breeze
Floating and dancing in the wind.
We stop and recall all memories
In these our autumn twilight years.

Who Am I? by Joseph Watters

Am I a number,
In a line that never ends,
Am I a single cell,
One in a million, that all depends.

Am I brave,
Or am I stupid,
Based on a close shave,
Or was I too intrepid, only I know the answer to that.

Inside, only a few things count to me,
My friends, my family and God,
I do not want to die alone,
I need to find that social zone.

Am I an atom,
Out of an element,
In a way yes,
I do my part.

Am I a grain of wheat,
In a field of many brothers,
Am I unimportant,
Yes, without the others.

We are a union,
We are as one,
Without each other,
I am alone, just one.

I am clever, but I am stupid,
I am a believer, but I am a doubter,
I am for real, but I am a faker,
Who am I? I am the one and only...
Me!

My Dignity and Respect by Margaret Eccles

D – Do I <u>Deserve</u> to be listened to, instead of feeling <u>dejected</u> and <u>depressed</u>.

I – I need to feel <u>impressed</u> and admired, that I could talk to you,as you did listen.

G – I have felt <u>guilty</u> for too long, I need to <u>grow</u> in confidence.

N – No feeling,<u>neglected.</u> I am more <u>nourished</u> as a person and not just a patient.

I – I, an <u>individual</u> as you are. I respect you as you respect me.

T – <u>Today</u> I <u>thrive,</u> a strength gaining, a wellbeing growing. You're helping me to share my fears, <u>thoughts,</u> feelings.

One in Four People, sometime in their lives, will experience a mental health problem and may need to accept treatment and support.

Y – Yesterday I did.

Chapter 14 – My Year of Writing
Carol Ross

When my son asked me to write stories with him one half-term holiday (February 2005), I said yes darn quick – anything to get a boy writing! But neither of us could have imagined what it would eventually lead to. His story – *There's a Roman in My Garden* – was written, typed and illustrated before he went back to school. Mine kept growing, and before long I had 14 chapters of a children's book. And this after 20 years of doing almost no creative writing! Once I started writing creatively again, I came to realise the power writing has for making you feel better. I continued writing, and also began studying creative and therapeutic writing, counselling and personal development.

Then in September 2009, my employer (Cumbria Partnership NHS Foundation Trust) launched a competition similar to the BBC's Dragons' Den (BBC, 2012). When I saw the competition poster I had an idea for a writing project. I developed a proposal for a 'Cumbria Partnership Year of Writing', got shortlisted, pitched to the 'Dragons', and won funding to increase my hours for a year to undertake the project (Ross, 2012). The wave of adrenaline then abated, and the sleepless nights, hard work and long hours began! But it was all worth it – the project has touched so many people's lives (probably over 300), and has changed my life.

Aims and scope

My hopes for Cumbria Partnership Year of Writing were that it would be inspirational, educational and above all inclusive. I wanted the project to benefit as many of our patients (service users), carers and staff as possible, and I wanted groups to meet on equal terms – with no sense of 'us and them'.

I was sure that creative writing workshops should be included in the project, but most of all, I wanted to start writing sessions for patients in mental health wards (see Chapter 5). My hope was to inspire patients to start writing: to help their recovery; as a hobby for hospital and home; and so they might redefine themselves, if only in a small way, as writers rather than as people with this diagnosis or that.

To maximise the ongoing effects of the project, I felt I needed to include staff development opportunities, e.g., to develop skills in therapeutic writing. Through consultation with staff, I identified a list of workshop topics, and clinicians to lead them.

Events

The Year of Writing included 30 events: nine creative writing workshops (attended by 65 people; mainly service users, carers and staff of the trust and local voluntary organisations); five staff workshops (52 attended); 13 sessions in an adult acute mental health ward (20 patients each attended one to five sessions); two short writing 'taster' sessions (attended by 19 carers, 12 trust staff and two staff of a local voluntary organisation) and a conference (Ross, 2011).

Creative writing workshops

The programme I developed for the creative writing workshops comprised: introductions; brief explanation of the Year of Writing and how writing can benefit wellbeing; 5- to 10-minute 'freewriting' exercises (with or without verbal prompts); journal writing exercises; longer writing exercises using stimuli such as objects or pictures; reading aloud (with no pressure to do so); and group discussions. A warm, informal approach was adopted, with an emphasis on forming safe, caring groups to encourage sharing and a feeling of acceptance.

These are some comments from workshop attendees:

"This has been brilliant! I would love more of this and would love to encourage carers to access this workshop. The sharing of ideas by people in this group has been inspiring."

"It allowed me to be reflective and look at where I am at and work out why I had spontaneously written what I did and what I needed to do."

"Once I had started things came back to me that have been locked away for so long."

"The written word can be very powerful, vicarious experience gained from reading a book can be the means for the release of a range of different feelings which may be not just be therapeutic but also offers hope and solutions. Someone has to write the book, it is a shared intimate relationship between the writer and the reader. A particular letter or story can have meaning for the reader as long as it exists. It can be read a 1000 times. To write can be a most rewarding and fulfilling task giving a person a sense of self and achievement. The written word can exist without a reader, the simple fact of writing thus becomes an opportunity for self-expression."

In the first workshop we wrote this collaborative poem:

Life is...

Life is breathing in and breathing out
　　　an amazing journey
　　　　　the road to your dreams

Life is so precious
　　　not a rehearsal
　　　　　full of ups and downs
　　　　　　　14 years and out for good behaviour

Life is going out to the pub
　　　the warm glow of a friendly fire
　　　　　a mixture of emotions
　　　　　　　complicated

Life is not what I expected
　　　an experiment for the next chapter
　　　　　the only thing that is truly yours

Life is what life is all about

To produce the poem I first asked each participant to write three lines starting with *"Life is..."* on strips of coloured paper. Then as a group we chose the line we liked best from each person. Finally my co-facilitator, Marilyn Messenger, and I arranged the lines into a poem, which we read aloud in the group and published in a Year of Writing newsletter.

Ward writing groups – see Chapter 5 (also Ross, 2011).

Staff workshops

The staff workshops included half days on writing for publication and running reflective practice groups, and a development day for 17 members of a community mental health team that combined therapeutic and reflective writing exercises with group work on writing good patient notes. Staff attending the team development day all made pledges saying what they had been inspired to do differently in the future.

Writing in Healthcare Conference (held 18 March 2011)

What was originally planned as a continuing professional development (CPD) conference for around 100 staff, ended up being attended by a marvellously diverse and enthusiastic group of 134 people, including staff, service users and carers. Many people have enthused about the day and said it was both enjoyable and inspiring. For me, it was a magical day, marred only by the sad fact that I can only be in one place at once and so was unable to attend **all** the workshops, which ran in parallel.

I am grateful to a lot of people whose support made the day such a success, in particular the workshop leaders:

- Reflective practice writing and therapeutic creative writing (Gillie Bolton)

- Write it out! The positive power of creative word-play. Creative writing for personal growth and stress management (Geraldine Green)

- I'm still me – the importance of the written word in life story work (Sandi Winterhalder and Helen Jackman)

- Working with narratives in child and adolescent mental health services (Alison Burgess and Jennifer Atkinson)
- Running a reflective practice group (Kathryn McDowell, John Masson and Shaun Cavanagh)
- Poetry and collaborative poems in group work (Nigel Peirce and Liz Fitton)
- Introduction to writing for publication (Dave Dagnan)
- Research presentation/research clinic (Angus Forsyth and Dave Dagnan)

Communications

Communications were key to the success of the project and in this I had the very welcome assistance of our Communications Team who helped me to develop a communications strategy and publicised the project through news releases.

I produced newsletters and reports and maintained web pages throughout the project to keep people informed.

Reflections

When the Year of Writing ended I was so wrapped up in the project that I found it extremely difficult to let go of the various activities I had been involved in. A period of reflection was needed, around what was best for me and my family, before I managed to decide how to proceed, i.e., which activities to continue, unpaid if necessary, because they were important to me personally, and which I needed to stop.

The activities I found the most personally rewarding and beneficial for participants were the ward writing sessions, so I was delighted when these re-commenced in April 2011 at the request of the Ward Manager. I have been added to the trust's 'bank staff' as a Writing Practitioner and am now paid at an hourly rate for my writing sessions by individual wards/units.

In September 2011, I started to lead a weekly writing group in the Psychiatric Intensive Care Unit (PICU). I also now lead a monthly writing group for discharged patients and anyone else who feels that writing might help their health and wellbeing.

From my point-of-view, the Cumbria Partnership Year of Writing started in September 2009 when I wrote the bid for funding and ended with the Writing and Healthcare Conference in March 2011. But, as I said at the beginning of this chapter, my journey in therapeutic writing really began in February 2005 and it is still continuing. I have learned so much in the last six or so years, especially in the last 18 months, and I continue to learn more with every session I lead and every article and book I read on the subject. The Year of Writing project has turned a casual interest in therapeutic writing into my passion, and changed my life – thank you Dragons!

References

BBC. (2012). *Dragons' Den*. Retrieved 20 January, 2012, from http://www.bbc.co.uk/programmes/b006vq92

Ross, C. A. (2011). Evaluation of Cumbria Partnership Year of Writing workshops. *Cumbria Partnership Journal of Research, Practice and Learning, 1*, 17-20. Retrieved 27 May 2011, from http://www.cumbriapartnership.nhs.uk/uploads/Journal/CPJRPL%201%201%20Spring%202011%20p17%20Evaluation.pdf

Ross, C. A. (2012). *Words for Wellbeing*. Retrieved 22 January 2012 from http://www.cumbriapartnership.nhs.uk/words-for-well being.htm

Appendix: Year of Writing timeline

September 2009	Cumbria Partnership 'Dragons Den' publicised Discussions with clinicians and service users Started to develop proposal
October 2009	Submitted proposal to shortlisting team
November 2009	Informed proposal had been shortlisted Prepared presentation Entered the 'Dragons Den'
December 2009	Funding awarded to Year of Writing project Started attending relevant training courses
January – March 2010	Planning meetings held for all aspects of the project Developed detailed project plan Developed communications strategy Conducted staff survey about project scope Contacted ward managers about writing sessions Started identifying leaders for workshops Booked conference venue and main tutor Started promotion of workshops and conference Started developing web page and handouts
April 2010	Year of Writing officially started Weekly writing sessions began in one ward Year of Writing newsletter issued
May 2010	Planning and promotion of creative writing workshops
June 2010	First creative writing workshop (full day, Penrith) Staff workshop – writing for publication and reflective practice (full day, Penrith) Short creative writing session at a relaxation day (1 hour, Whitehaven)

	Creative writing 'taster' for staff (½ hour, Carlisle) Year of Writing newsletter issued
July 2010	Staff workshop – therapeutic writing (full day, Penrith)
August 2010	Ward writing sessions ended to release time for organisation of conference
September 2010	Creative writing workshop (½ day, Barrow-in-Furness) Staff session on reflective writing (1 hour, Carlisle) Creative writing session for carers (2 hours, Penrith) Year of Writing newsletter issued
October 2010	Creative writing workshop (½ day, Carlisle) Creative writing workshop (½ day, Distington) Short creative writing workshop (1 hour, Barrow-in-Furness) Team development day held (Whitehaven) Issued a ½ year report on progress News release about conference issued (national) Article published in North West NHS Bulletin
November 2010	Two creative writing workshops (½ day each, Carlisle) Writing 'Taster' session for a carers' group (½ hour, Carlisle) News release about Year of Writing issued (local) Item about Year of Writing published in Cumberland News
December 2010	Staff workshop – writing for publication (½ day, Carlisle)

January 2011	Priority switched to conference planning
	Promotion of conference
	Finalisation of programme
	Taking bookings
	News release about conference issued
February 2011	Creative writing workshop (½ day, Whitehaven)
	Conference programme sent to printers
	Conference bookings increasing
	Planned arrangements with venue
	Allocated workshops to rooms
	Set maximum delegate numbers for each conference workshop
	Article published in Cumbria Partnership Journal of Research, Practice and Learning
	Year of Writing newsletter issued
March 2011	Last minute planning for conference
	Production of badges and handout packs
	Photographer booked
	News release about conference issued
	Conference held
	Short item about conference on local radio
	Year of Writing officially ended
April 2011	Priority switched to production of this book
	Year of Writing web page changed to 'Words for Wellbeing'
	Ward writing sessions re-commenced

Recovery by Peter Taylor

Flying high and coming down
Change from a smile to a frown
Look at the sky and see a cloud
Hanging over earth like a shroud
In this depressive state I do miss
Last night's dream of an angel's kiss.

Up and down, a mad hatter's smile
And my flashing thoughts do beguile
For manic hours my florid state
Controls me and makes me wait
For a precious moment's blissful peace
From racing thoughts that do not cease
I think of a skull speaking in my ear
And for my sanity I do fear.

I wish I could be normal just like you
To find some solace from moods blue
This psychotic state cannot last
Hope one day my woes will pass
And I will come and speak to you
Of mutual dreams that might come true.

Maybe one day soon I will find
Peace at last for my strange mind.

List of Contributors

Adam

Robert Armitage

Autumn Leaves Day Care Group is a group of people aged between 76 and 94. They called their group 'Autumn Leaves' because they don't believe they have entered their winter time yet.

Colin Bentham is the Artist in Residence for St Matthew's in Barrow-in-Furness. He graduated as a mature student in 2004 from UCLAN in Preston. Colin also received a Millennium Award for a project he did at Furness General Hospital, where he created several large colourful paintings as way-points to help people find their way around.

John Berry was left with memory and speech difficulties after suffering a Brain Trauma from a serious accident. His therapists suggested that writing would help him. Writing proved to be a huge help in his recovery and self motivation. John feels that writing has been a huge benefit both for his speech and memory problems and for himself. John is now writing a book.

Dr Gillie Bolton has been working with reflective, reflexive and healing writing for over 25 years, having found that it really benefitted herself – writing in her own journal nearly every day. An award-winning poet, author of books, academic and professional papers including journals such as The Lancet (for all information: www.gilliebolton.com). Educated at Cambridge University and University of East Anglia Medical School, Gillie lives in Bloomsbury London and the Hope Valley Derbyshire with as many of her three little grandchildren staying as possible.

Leona Byers is a 15-year-old schoolgirl who dedicates this poem to all who have supported her. She finds joy in writing poetry and spending time with friends and family.

Julie Callan loves Chinese poetry and culture. On a recent trip to Wulong Panda Conservation Centre, Chengdu, China, she was lucky enough to get to hug a baby panda. "I hugged a panda!" has since become her mantra.

Steve Childerley lives on his own in Penrith. He loves walking in The North Pennines and the Lake District, collecting photographs of Cumbria and The Scottish Highlands, and writing poetry.

Pam Clatworthy is a retired head of Gosforth Primary School, West Cumbria. Three years ago (at the time of writing), Pam was diagnosed with heart problems and had to have a quadruple heart by-pass. Pam says she cannot express her gratitude to the wonderful NHS staff who took such trouble with an elderly woman. The staff of Pam's local health centre at Seascale, the West Cumberland Hospital in Whitehaven and the wonderful James Cook Hospital in Middlesbrough. Pam says that they gave her first class treatment with love in their hearts. Since making a good recovery Pam has rejoiced every day in the fact that she is alive and well and able to appreciate the beauty of the local countryside.

Julia Clifford lives in the village of Swarthmoor. She has a beautiful Council bungalow that she shares with three pet rabbits who she absolutely adores. Julia's other hobbies apart from writing include reading and weaving. She also attends the Shine Art project in Barrow.

Donna-Louise Curwen says of herself: "Mammy, mam, mama this is who I am. Through those titles I hold the most rewarding job in the world. I may not always get it right but I can honestly say I try my very best. My children make me so proud and I love and adore Molly and Isaac with all that I am."

Grace Deakin, age 93, lives alone, but with her family next door, and has home-care three times a day. Due to poor eyesight and arthritis she is no longer able to maintain her passion for needlework but feels "adequate for my age" and still enjoys writing.

Margaret Eccles is a Service User who lives in West Cumbria.

Penelope Elias says of herself: "Writing about my experiences has helped me make sense of them and move on. It has also given me greater confidence. I believe that everyone has a creative urge in some capacity. Being encouraged to explore this can be transformational."

Victoria Field is a Certified Poetry Therapist. She has co-edited three books on therapeutic writing, most recently Writing Routes from Jessica Kingsley. Her creative work includes two collections of poetry, one based on a residency at Truro Cathedral and two plays produced by Hall for Cornwall. Victoria was a Hawthornden Fellow in 2012.

Elizabeth Gates. With a BA Honours in English Language and Literature, an MA in Linguistics, 25 years' experience as a published health and well-being writer and 10 years in adult education (in the UK, Belgium and Germany), Elizabeth Gates is well equipped to facilitate creative writing and Story workshops in healthcare and social care for individuals and groups. And, in 2005, she founded her writing and communication consultancy – which promotes the use of storytelling and creative writing in a variety of settings. For further information about Lonely Furrow Company and testimonials, please see Elizabeth's Story-telling and Writing for Wellbeing blog: http://lightforshadows.wordpress and her brochure website: http://www.lonelyfurrowcompany.com

Alison Gawne lives in the Lake District. She has two beautiful children, Joe and Ellie. She loves many sports, socialising with her lovely friends and family, and walking in the countryside with her dog, Alfie.

Gayle is a loving mum and keen artist who aspires to be an Art Therapist.

Lorraine Gibbard has found poetry to be a cathartic occupation during her years as a mental health service user, but unsure of their interest to other people She offers her poem Relapse hesitantly, hoping that it may be of use.

Jill Goulden lives happily in a small village near Millom, close to the sea and the hills.

Judy Gray lives West Cumbria with her husband. She is passionate about the countryside and wildlife and is a keen conservationist. Favourite pastimes are writing letters, poetry, and family and social history.

Geraldine Green. Ulverston poet Dr Geraldine Green lives with husband Geoff and Border collie Roy. She's a published poet, university lecturer, freelance creative writing tutor, mentor and associate editor of Poetry Bay www.poetrybay.com.

Lee Habbershon has many interests including Art and reading about History, Egyptology and Psychology. She has in the past exhibited artwork and poetry about Dissociative Identity Disorder (DID) and child abuse, both of which were published. Lee also set up an organisation (now defunct) in the Kendal area with the aim of educating NHS staff, students and other interested parties about psychological problems and crises as experienced by the sufferer.

Declan Hall was 7-years old when he wrote "Me".

Stephen Hanley is a music composer and artist (portraits). He is working on becoming a successful composer writing music for TV and film, and drawing animal and human portraits in his spare time. You can find Stephen on Facebook.

Vee Howard-Jones is a Lecturer, Counsellor and Supervisor. Her interests are using metaphor and imagery therapeutically with clients through the media of talk, books, poetry, creative writing, and watching films – all of the things she was passionate about as a little girl – and the passion has never waned! She describes her therapeutic work as always a fascination, a privilege and foreverly fulfillingmost.

Linda M. Hughes

Lucy Hutton's daughter was a baby when she wrote the poem Bang Flash.

Patricia Jackson lives with her husband at Burgh by Sands. They have two lovely border collies called Sam and Tess with huge personalities who like romping around Burgh Marsh and like to think they're 'boss'! She has taken up lawn bowling over the past few years which can be seen as a genteel sport but Patricia says is hugely competitive!

Laura Jobson, Mum of James, born October 2011.

Suzanne Kelsey was born and educated in Cumbria and went on to study dance, drama and music in the South. After living and teaching in the Midlands for many years, Suzanne returned to Cumbria in 1989, and became a lecturer in further and higher education. Always very proactive about her health, Suzanne was greatly shocked in 2009 to be diagnosed with a serious viral heart condition that led to myocarditis and then to cardiomyopathy. Needing to stop all her vigorous exercise and activities and take up a quiet therapeutic activity, Suzanne returned to her love of poetry and she found that poetry gave her time to look within and reflect on life. Suzanne then had the idea to raise money through her poetry. On July 14th 2009 she launched her first poetry book *Echoes*, followed by *Threads* and *Serendipity*. She has raised over £4,500 to date by giving talks, reciting her poetry and selling the books.

Jessica Mary Lucas is from Manchester and came to Carlisle to study for a BA in Digital Arts at the University of Cumbria, specialising in digital painting and illustration. She enjoys costume design, cartoons, script-writing and photography. She goes by the alias of Jessica on Paper.

John Masson is currently working as a clinical psychologist in the NHS. He has enjoyed poetry since he was at school when he first read Wilfred Owen and R. S. Thomas who remain his favourite poets.

Debbie Mayes says of herself: "I have bipolar disorder which means my mood can vary from elation to depression with stable periods in between. It has been recognised that through history some bipolar people have been extremely creative. I am also creative enjoying producing works of art and poetry. So it seems to me that being bipolar is a mixed blessing, the mood swings are very difficult to live with, but I wouldn't want to lose my creative self. My partner and I moved to Kendal from London three years ago and are very happy here. I work part time at Lancaster University as a service user researcher."

Marilyn Messenger was born in Yorkshire and lives in Cumbria. She is attracted to life's quirkiness or unlikely connections and if humour sneaks in then so much the better. She relishes the diversity of working in different genres which to date have included fiction, non-fiction, advertising slogans, comedy sketches and poetry plus radio, film and graphic novel scripts. She is currently writing a radio drama script alongside several short stories.

Katie Metcalfe is a Teesside author of two books on anorexia and two poetry collections: *One of Many Knots* and *Outskirts*. She is the creator and editor of *Beautiful Scruffiness* Literary Magazine. Her poetry and fiction has been published in various anthologies and magazines including: *Ink on Paper Poetry/Art Anthology*, *The Wilds Anthology*, *Discoveries Short Story Anthology*, *Ten by Ten Poetry Anthology*, *Kenaz Creative Writing Magazine*, *Black Light Engine Room Literary Journal*, *Sentinal Literary Journal*, *Teesside Artists' Journal* and *Exposure*. Katie is currently working on a novel. http://katiemetcalfe.wordpress.com/

Dave Miller is a service user who has found the writing experience both fulfilling and therapeutic.

Andy Mortimer is a photographer who lives beside Morecambe Bay and frequently joins the cross-bay walk with his neighbour Cedric Robinson, the Queen's Guide to the Sands.

Eileen Norman was born in Lancashire, brought up in the West Country, and has been at home in Cumbria for 30 years. Mother to three boys, Grannie to big twin boys and a little girl. Loves retirement and travelling in the camper van with husband when other commitments allow!

Eileen O'Reilly holds a certificate in social work and is a qualified teacher. She has worked in schools across the UK and had the privilege of teaching in Addis Abbaba, Ethiopia, during which time she enjoyed learning and living in a different culture. Eileen is presently a Motivational Speaker/Life Coach/NLP Master Practioner. She has worked predominantly in the Cumbria area and is expanding her career throughout the UK (for further details please see her website www.exerciseyoursoul.com). Eileen has written her autobiography entitled, "Please, please don't let go of my hand" (soon to be published) and is presently writing the sequel. She has lived in Holland and briefly in Perth, Western Australia, where she spent some time travelling along the coast and the Outback. Her main ambition is to "write, speak and travel."

Hazel C. Perry lives in Carlisle and enjoys walking, cooking and baking, and looking after her home and family.

Christopher Pilling was born in 1936. He taught French and PE on the Wirral, in Yorkshire and in Cumbria. He played squash for Cumbria veterans. He is a poet and translator, mainly from the French. *Coming Ready or Not* includes his early collections of poems and new work. He won the John Dryden Award for his versions of Catullus, and the Kate Collingwood Award for his play about the Spanish Inquisition. His translations of Tristan Corbière, Max Jacob, Lucien Becker and Maurice Carême are also obtainable via email to: chrispilling@onetel.com

Ian Richmond retired to the area in 2010 after a career in marketing communications. He has since spent his time in voluntary work including a spell as a volunteer with Cumbria Partnership NHS Foundation Trust.

Carol Ross was born in Yorkshire and has lived in Cumbria since 1995. With a passion for learning, Carol followed her BSc Honours degree in Biochemistry from Manchester University with a number of other qualifications including creative writing and counselling. She has worked in publishing, information science and, more recently, clinical audit. Since 2010, Carol has been leading weekly writing groups for mental health inpatients. Carol has had some non-fiction work published and two of her poems appeared in *Pinhole Camera: The Third Side of the Coin* (University of Cumbria). Email: writing.year@cumbria.nhs.uk; web pages: http://www.cumbriapartnership.nhs.uk/words-for-wellbeing.htm and http://trioross.wordpress.com/.

Lisa Rossetti is a coach and coach-supervisor, as well as a writer and story practitioner. Working mostly in health and social settings, she uses storytelling and creative writing for mental wellbeing. She also uses writing and story techniques for personal and organisational development as a way of nurturing innovative thinking, growth, wellbeing and teamwork. She is founder of The Story Café, a workshop for personal growth and wellbeing. She is currently training to use creative story interventions with dementia sufferers. Lisa has trained coaches, counsellors and social workers to use story approaches and creative writing interventions in their work. Lisa is a member of Lapidus and NAWE, and a partner with the NHS Year of Health and Wellbeing 2012 in the North West. Lisa can be contacted via www.positivelives.co.uk, Twitter @lisarossetti or on 07815 888803.

Fernando Smith is a poet, painter and singer-songwriter living in Cumbria. In addition to performing his work across the UK, he has worked with families, children and young people deemed at risk, including children who have suffered abuse, young people in care and people on the fringes of society. He currently works for Shelter – the National Campaign for the Homeless, running their children and families support and therapeutic services across Scotland. The poem First Lapwings is from the book *Welcome to the Golden Life* (2010) by Fernando Smith, www.fernandosmith.co.uk

Sylvia Stevens has lived in Cumbria for 20 years with her husband. She draws inspiration from the landscape for her poetry, short stories and watercolour painting. She enjoys music and is a keen fell walker.

Hilary Tattershall

Peter Taylor lives in Carlisle and enjoys walking, reading and listening to music. His poem 'Recovery' is drawn from experience of mental illness.

Elaine Trevitt is retired from the practice of osteopathy and now concentrates on two other therapeutic activities, gardening and writing. These come together in her work as editor of the newsletter for the Cumbria Group of the Hardy Plants Society, where she encourages others to write about their passion.

Joseph Watters is a secondary school pupil who was studying for his GCSEs at the time he wrote his poem "Who Am I?". He is a keen musician with an aspiration to become a teacher.

Andy Wild is Hayley's dad.

Ann Wilson hosts the spoken word open mic at The Brewery Arts Centre and works as a poet and facilitator on community projects. You can read more of her writing at www.annthepoet.com.